SIMPLIFIED PHYSICS FOR RADIOLOGY STUDENTS

SIMPLIFIED PHYSICS FOR RADIOLOGY STUDENTS

By

BARBARA HOWL, M.S.R.T., S.R.R.

Wolverhampton, Staffordshire
England
Formerly, Chief Technician in Radiation Therapy
Vanderbilt University Hospital
Nashville, Tennessee

CHARLES C THOMAS · PUBLISHER
Springfield • Illinois • U.S.A.

Published and Distributed Throughout the World by
CHARLES C THOMAS • PUBLISHER
BANNERSTONE HOUSE
301-327 East Lawrence Avenue, Springfield, Illinois, U.S.A.
NATCHEZ PLANTATION HOUSE
735 North Atlantic Boulevard, Fort Lauderdale, Florida, U.S.A.

Library of Congress Catalog Card Number: 78-161163

With THOMAS BOOKS *careful attention is given to all details of manufacturing and design. It is the Publisher's desire to present books that are satisfactory as to their physical qualities and artistic possibilities and appropriate for their particular use.* THOMAS BOOKS *will be true to those laws of quality that assure a good name and good will.*

Printed in the United States of America

HH-11

TO

My Parents, who gave me a great deal of encouragement, and the Students and Technicians of The Division of Radiotherapy at Vanderbilt University Hospital, Nashville, Tennessee, who were willing guinea pigs!

Introduction

Many people find that they need a textbook of very basic physics, either when they start their study of radiologic physics or when they return to it years later. This book will, I hope, fill that need. It is written in very simple language and explains the basic principles rather than the scientific intricacies.

Further information can be obtained from the many excellent text books that give fuller and deeper information on the subject. The two most suitable books for further study are, in my opinion,

1. Selman, Joseph: *The Basic Physics of Radiation Therapy*. Springfield, Thomas, 1960.
2. Selman, Joseph: *The Fundamentals of X-Ray and Radium Physics*, 4th ed., 8th printing. Springfield, Thomas, 1970.

Wolverhampton, Staffordshire, England B.H. □

Contents

SIMPLIFIED PHYSICS FOR RADIOLOGY STUDENTS

1 Atoms

Every substance in the world is built up of units called **atoms.**

Structure of the Atom

An atom resembles a solar system in its structure (Fig. 1). A solar system consists of a sun around which planets move in set paths called orbits. In an atom the sun is represented by the nucleus and the planets are represented by electrons.

Nucleus

The nucleus is made up of two main types of particles: protons and neutrons.

a. *Proton.* A proton is a particle that carries a single, positive electric charge. In size it is 1,850 times as large as an electron.

b. *Neutron.* A neutron is a particle which is the same size as a proton but does not carry an electric charge. It is, therefore, neutral. Protons and neutrons are so much more massive than electrons that all the mass of the atom is considered to be in the nucleus.

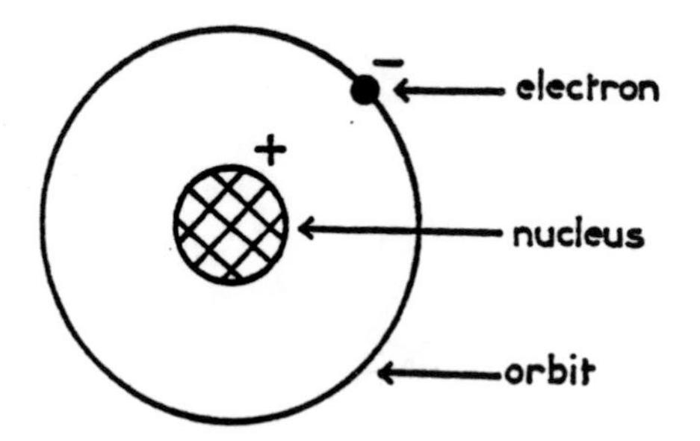

Figure 1. Basic parts of an atom.

Electrons

An electron is a particle that orbits the nucleus of an atom. It is 1,850 times smaller than either a proton or a neutron. Despite its minute size, it carries a single, negative electric charge.

An atom in a normal, stable state is electrically neutral. Thus, the positively charged protons in the nucleus must be balanced by an equal number of negatively charged electrons. The electrons move constantly around the nucleus in paths called orbits, or shells. Each electron tends to follow a constant orbital path.

Shells

Orbits are commonly referred to as shells. A shell is not a solid object, only the path followed by an electron. Each atom has a certain number of electrons in orbit, that is, the same number as the number of protons in the nucleus. Atoms which have more than two electrons in orbit must have extra layers of shells.

Each shell is labeled by a letter of the alphabet. The shell nearest

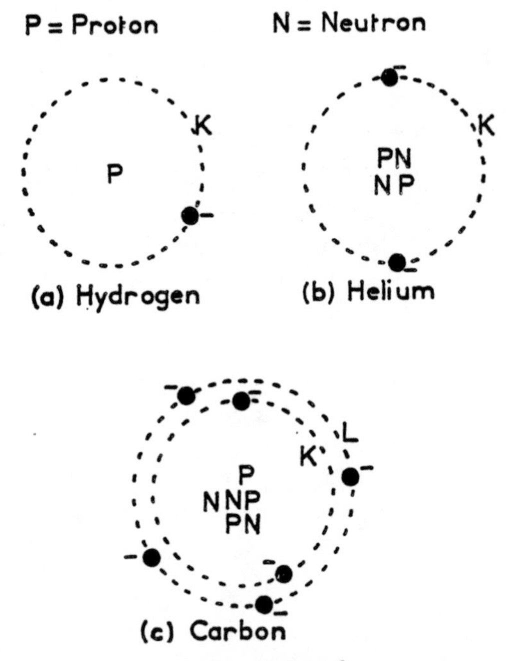

Figure 2. Structure of atoms.

the nucleus is the K-shell, the next further out is the L-shell, the next the M-shell, and so on (Fig. 2). Each shell can hold only a certain number of electrons:

The K-shell can hold 2 electrons.
The L-shell can hold 8 electrons.
The M-shell can hold 18 electrons.
The N-shell can hold 32 electrons.

Binding Energy

Each shell has a certain energy associated with it, called the binding energy. (Imagine that the nucleus is a magnet. Objects moving around this magnet would be attracted to it with a certain force. This force is represented by the binding energy.) The electrons in the shells are negatively charged and the binding energy is negative energy. The inner shells have a greater binding energy than the outer shells. (Again the analogy to a magnet helps: the nearer an object is to a magnet, the more strongly it is attracted.)

The binding energy of any particular shell is the same for that shell in all the atoms of the same substance. Example: The binding energy of the K-shell of an atom of lead is the same on the K-shell of any other lead atom; however, the binding energy of the K-shell of an atom of lead is not the same as the binding energy of the K-shell of an atom of carbon, or silver. (Imagine again that the nucleus is a magnet. A larger nucleus will exert a larger attractive force over its electrons than a smaller one. Thus the binding energies will be different.)

Atomic Number

Each atom is given an atomic number. This number is given the symbol Z. The atomic number is the same as the number of protons in the nucleus; therefore, a particular substance always has the same atomic number. The atomic number identifies the substance chemically. Example: Carbon always has the atomic number 6 or, conversely, an atom which has an atomic number 6 is always carbon.

Element

A substance that is made up of atoms which all have the same atomic number is called an element. Example: A collection of carbon atoms makes up the element carbon.

Physical Property

The physical properties of a substance are those which indicate the physical state of the substance. For example, whether it is a solid, a liquid, or a gas.

Chemical Property

The chemical properties of a substance state how it reacts with other substances. Example: What happens when sodium is placed in water.

Periodic Table

When elements are placed in order of their atomic number they are found to fall into certain definite groups, according to their chemical and physical properties. They can then be arranged in a special way. This arrangement is known as the Periodic Table (Fig. 3).

Chemical Symbols

All elements are given a "shorthand" name called a chemical symbol. The following is a shortened list of elements, together

	GROUPS								
PERIOD	I	II	III	IV	V	VI	VII	VIII	O
1	H(1)								He(2)
2	Li(3)	Be(4)	B(5)	C(6)	N(7)	O(8)			Ne(10)
3	Na(11)		Al(13)		P(15)	S(16)	Cl(17)		A(18)
4	K(19) Cu(29)	Ca(20) Zn(30)				Se(34)	Br(35)	Co(27)	Kr(36)
5	Ag(47)	Sr(38)		Sn(50)		Mo(42) Te(52)	Tc(43) I(53)		Xe(54)
6	Cs(55) Au(79)	Ba(56) Hg(80)		Pb(82)	Bi(83)	W(74) Po(84)		Pt(78)	Rn(86)
7		Ra(88)				U(92)			

Figure 3. Simplified periodic table. ( )=atomic number.

with their chemical symbols. They are those elements most likely to be met with in radiology.

aluminum — Al	hydrogen — H	potassium — K
antimony — Sb	iodine — I	radium — Ra
argon — Ar(A)	iridium — Ir	radon — Rn
barium — Ba	iron — Fe	selenium—Se
bismuth — Bi	krypton — Kr	silver — Ag
beryllium — Be	lead — Pb	sodium — Na
boron — B	lithium — Li	strontium — Sr
bromine — Br	mercury — Hg	sulphur — S
calcium — Ca	molybdenum — Mo	technetium — Tc
carbon — C	nickel — Ni	tellurium — Te
cesium — Cs	nitrogen — N	tin — Sn
chlorine — Cl	neon — Ne	tungsten — W
cobalt — Co	oxygen — O	uranium — U
copper — Cu	phosphorus — P	xenon — Xe
helium — He	platinum — Pt	zinc — Zn
gold — Au	polonium — Po	

Mixture

When two or more elements are placed together but retain their separate identities they are said to form a mixture. Each element still has its own chemical and physical properties.

Compound

When two elements are placed together and react with each other to form a third, different substance they are said to have formed a compound. Example: Hydrogen and oxygen react to form water. A compound can be formed from the combination of more than two elements. Example: Magnesium carbonate is formed from magnesium, carbon, and oxygen.

A compound does not have the same properties as the elements that combined to form it. Example: Water is formed from hydrogen and oxygen, which are both gases at atmospheric temperature and pressure, but water is a liquid.

Chemical symbols are used to represent compounds as well as elements. Example: Water is shown as H_2O. This tells you not only that it is formed from hydrogen and oxygen but also that they are combined together in the ratio of two atoms of hydrogen to one atom of oxygen.

Molecule

The smallest part of a compound that can exist is called a molecule. Example: A molecule of water (H_2O) contains three atoms: two of hydrogen and one of oxygen.

Chemical Combination

If an atom, A, with an outer shell that contains one less electron than is possible meets an atom, B, with only one electron in its outer shell, then A will attract the electron from B. This means that A has gained an extra negative charge, the electron, and the atom now has an overall negative charge. Similarly B has lost a negative charge and has, in consequence, an overall positive charge. Since a positive charge will attract a negative charge A and B will be attracted to each other and end up sharing the electron. They have combined by mutual attraction to form a compound, AB. Written as a formula: $A + B = AB$

An atom that has a full outer shell will tend not to react with any other atom. It is said to be inert. An atom that has a deficiency in the possible number of electrons in the outer shell will react with one or more other atoms in an attempt to fill its outer shell. Thus you can see that the chemical properties of an element depend on the number of electrons in the outer shell.

Valency

Valency is the combining power of an atom. It depends on either the number of electrons in the outer shell or the number of possible gaps in the outer shell. The official definition is that valency is the number of atoms of hydrogen that will combine with any particular atom. This is because hydrogen is a sort of "basic atom" in that it has one electron and one possible gap in its shell.

Mass Number

The mass of an atom is made up of the total number of particles in the nucleus. The mass of the electrons is so small that it can be ignored. The mass number of the atom is the total number of protons and neutrons. Example: The carbon nucleus is composed of six protons and six neutrons. Its mass number is therefore 12. Mass number is given the symbol A.

Atomic Weight

Because the mass, and therefore the weight, of the electrons is negligible, the mass number and the atomic weight are more or less the same. The mass number is often called the atomic weight. However, because of the presence of isotopes in an element, the atomic weight is actually an average of several slightly differing weights, and is not necessarily a whole number. Example: The atomic weight of chlorine is 35.5.

A better definition is that atomic weight is the weight of an atom compared with the weight of an atom of carbon. The atomic weight of carbon is 12. (In the past both hydrogen and oxygen have been used as standards but carbon is found to be more accurate.)

Isotope

An isotope is an atom of an element having the same atomic number as the other atoms of that element but a different mass number. This means that it has the same number of protons but either more or fewer neutrons. There are two sorts of isotopes.

1. *Stable Isotope*

Stable isotopes are the ones in which the numbers of protons and neutrons bear a stable relationship to each other.

2. *Unstable Isotope*

Unstable isotopes are the ones in which the numbers of protons and neutrons bear an unstable relationship to each other. Unstable isotopes are called radioactive isotopes or radioisotopes.

In an attempt to reach a stable state the nucleus ejects (or emits) particles. These particles cause "damage" to the surrounding atoms. This damage is called ionization. The damaging particles are then called ionizing radiations.

a. *Naturally Radioactive Radioisotopes.* These are found only among elements with an atomic number of 82 or more. In other words, they are elements with large numbers of particles in the nucleus.

b. *Artificially Produced Radioisotopes.* Any element can be made radioactive by bombarding its nuclei with protons or neutrons.

Nuclear Decay

The nucleus of a radioisotope will attempt to reach a stable state. This it does by one of three methods.

1. Alpha Emission

A nucleus possessing a large excess of particles will emit a "clump" of these particles. This consists of 2 protons and 2 neutrons. It is called an alpha particle. Two protons plus two neutrons also happens to be the composition of a helium nucleus. The alpha particle is represented symbolically as the Greek letter alpha, or as ${}_{2}He^{4}$, helium's symbol.

The emission of an alpha particle has two results: (a) The atomic number of the radioisotope is reduced by 2, thus forming a new element. (b) The mass number is reduced by 4. This process can be represented by a formula:

$${}_{88}Ra^{226} = {}_{2}He^{4} + {}_{86}Rn^{222}$$

${}_{88}Ra^{226}$ is the original radioisotope; ${}_{2}He^{4}$ is the particle emitted and ${}_{86}Rn^{222}$ is the new substance. A stream of alpha particles is called an alpha ray.

(*Note: Symbols.* Isotopes can be written in a form of shorthand. Instead of writing "cobalt with a mass number of 60," we write ${}^{60}Co$ [Sometimes you will see the older form Co^{60}]. This is the chemical symbol for cobalt with the mass number for that particular isotope of cobalt written as a superscript. There are other ways to represent this isotope. The approved way is

$${}^{60}_{27}Co$$

but because of the problems involved in setting into type a superscript over a subscript, you will usually see it printed in a book in this manner—${}_{27}Co^{60}$. The mass number is always the upper figure and the atomic number the lower. It is not usual to give the atomic number, as this is understood from the chemical symbol.)

2. *Beta Emission*

Beta particles are emitted in one of two ways.

a. *A neutron may split.* A neutron "splits" into a proton and an electron, thus increasing the atomic number by 1, although leaving the mass number the same. The element has now been altered chemically and has become a different element.

Example: $_{82}\text{Ra.B}^{214} = {}_{83}\text{Ra.C}^{214}$ + beta particle.

The symbol given to the beta particle is the Greek letter beta: β. The beta particle is the electron which was formed from the neutron and then emitted from the nucleus. Beta particles are emitted with varying amounts of energy. The more energy they possess the faster they move.

b. *A proton may split.* The result of this is that a proton disappears and a neutron and a positron are formed. A positron is a particle the same size as an electron but carrying a positive charge instead of a negative.

Electrically speaking, when a proton splits, a positive charge disappears and a neutral and a positive appear; that is, a proton disappears and a neutron and a positron are formed. The mass number again remains the same because, although a proton has disappeared, it has been replaced by a neutron. The atomic number falls by 1.

The positron is emitted from the nucleus just as the electron was in the previous case. A positron is a particle which does not normally exist in nature, so soon after its emission, it is neutralized by an electron. Before it is neutralized the energy of the positron is expended in causing ionization. As the positron is neutralized by the electron the mass of the positron and electron is converted into energy and emitted as a burst of radiation, called annihilation radiation.

3. *Gamma Emission*

When an alpha or beta particle is emitted, the nucleus is sometimes left in an excited state; that is, it is left with excess energy. This energy is given off as a burst of radiation called gamma radiation. This rarely happens when an alpha particle is emitted. It is mainly associated with beta particles.

Gamma radiation is made of energy only and is not a particle. It has no mass and no electric charge. It does not, therefore, affect either the mass or the charge of the nucleus.

Relative Penetrating Power of Radiations

Alpha particles are formed from 4 nuclear particles and are therefore relatively massive. They also carry a double, positive, charge. Because of this they are easily deflected and stopped by the atoms of any material that they attempt to penetrate. Even a high speed alpha particle can be stopped by a thin layer of paper.

Beta particles are very much smaller than alpha particles and carry only a single, negative, charge. They are therefore much less likely to be deflected by the atoms of the material through which they are passing. The penetrating power of a beta particle depends on the energy of the particle when it enters a material. It is, however, greater than that of an alpha particle.

Gamma radiation is energy only, has no mass or charge, and is therefore not deflected by the charges on the atoms of the material through which it is attempting to pass. The penetration of a gamma ray depends on the energy of the ray when it enters the absorbing material. A gamma ray will penetrate farther than a beta particle of the same energy, and very much farther than an alpha particle of the same energy.

Summary

Alpha and beta radiations are the means of transporting energy in the form of particles. As particles they have both mass and, in this case, charge and can be deflected by a magnetic or electric field.

Gamma radiation is the transfer of energy as energy. A gamma ray has neither mass nor charge and cannot be deflected by a magnetic or electric field.

Artifically Produced Radioisotopes

Any element can be made radioactive by bombarding the nuclei of its atoms with protons or neutrons; that is, by other nuclear particles. This can be done, for example, using a nuclear reactor or a cyclotron.

1. *Neutron Bombardment*

Neutrons may be inserted relatively easily into a nucleus, since they have no charge. They are not, therefore, repelled by the charge on the nucleus.

2. *Proton Bombardment*

Protons require great force for their insertion into a nucleus, since they are positively charged and are repelled by the charge on the nucleus at their approach. A great deal of force is needed to overcome this repulsion.

Decay

A nucleus that has been activated by neutron bombardment will decay by neutron disintegration. Similarly, a proton-activated nucleus will decay by proton disintegration. Example: Stable cobalt—^{59}Co—is activated by neutron bombardment and becomes radioactive ^{60}Co. ^{60}Co then decays by neutron disintegration to become ^{60}Ni.

Isobar

When two elements have the same mass number as each other, as, for example, ^{60}Co and ^{60}Ni, they are called isobars.

Half-Life

In any radioisotope the likelihood of any particular atom decaying is completely random. However, there is a period of time during which it can be predicted that half of the atoms will have decayed, even though which half is not known. This period is called the half-life. It is represented by the symbol $T^{1/2}$. Each radioisotope has a specific half-life. Example: ^{60}Co half-life is 5.3 years; ^{131}I half-life is 8 days. Different radioisotopes of the same element have different half-lives. Example: ^{60}Co has a half-life of 5.3 years; ^{58}Co has a half-life of 72 days.

Definition of Half-Life

The half-life is the time taken for the activity of a radioisotope to fall to half its original value. The half-life is said to have an exponential value. This means that the activity decays in a certain way: The original activity is 100%. The activity after one half-life is 50%. The activity after another half-life (2 half-lives) is ½ of 50%; that is, 25%. Similarly, the activity after 3 half-lives is ½ of 25%, that is, 12.5%.

Example: The half-life of ^{60}Co is 5.3 years. Suppose the original activity is 5,000 curies (Ci). The activity in 5.3 years (1 half-life) is 50% of 5,000; that is, 2,500 Ci. The activity in 10.6 years (2 half-lives) is 50% of 2,500; that is, 1,250 Ci. And so on.

2 Magnetism

CLASSIFICATION OF MAGNETS

A magnet is a substance that has the power to attract certain other substances. There are three different types.

1. *Natural Magnets*

a. *The Earth.* The earth has a natural magnetic field lying along a north-south axis.

b. *Lodestone.* Lodestone is iron ore which has become magnetized by lying in the earth's magnetic field for a long time.

2. *Artificial Magnets*

a. *Permanent Magnets.* Once they are magnetized, permanent magnets retain their magnetism and are difficult to demagnetize. Permanent magnets are made from materials which have a low permeability (are difficult to magnetize or demagnetize) and a high retentivity (are found to retain their magnetism). Example: Steel.

b. *Temporary Magnets.* These substances remain magnetized only while the magnetizing force is present. Once the inducing magnetic force is removed, the temporary magnet returns to a demagnetized state. These magnets are made from substances which have a high permeability and a low retentivity. That is, they are easy to magnetize but do not retain their magnetism. Example: Soft iron.

3. *Electromagnets*

When an electric current is passed through a coil of wire, a magnetic field is induced around the wire. If a bar of material

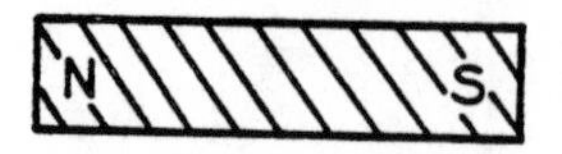

Figure 4. Bar magnet.

with high permeability (easily magnetized) is placed in the center of the coil of wire, it will become magnetized as long as the current is switched on. As soon as the current is switched off the magnetism will disappear. This is an electromagnet; that is, a magnet produced by electricity.

MAGNETIC PROPERTIES OF VARIOUS MATERIALS

Different materials are magnetized to different degrees.

1. *Ferromagnetic Materials*

Ferromagnetic materials make the best magnets. The name literally means materials containing iron (*ferro*: iron), but other metals have been found to act as well.

They all, in their natural state, have high permeability and low retentivity—they are easily magnetized and demagnetized. Examples: Soft iron, cobalt, and nickel.

They can be made into alloys with low permeability and high retentivity to be used as permanent magnets. Example: Steel.

2. *Paramagnetic Materials*

Paramagnetic materials can be magnetized with difficulty but, at best, make only weak magnets. Example: Platinum.

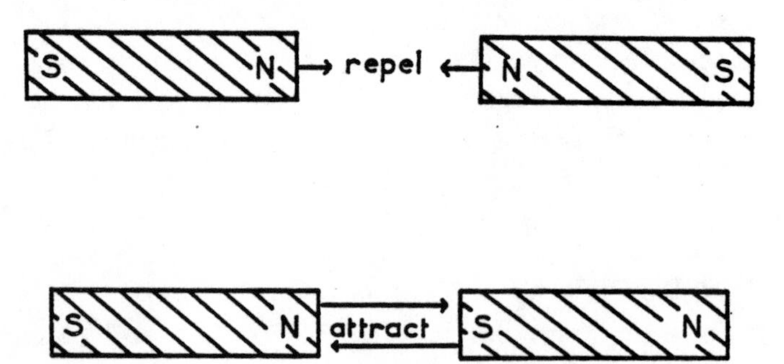

Figure 5.

3. *Nonmagnetic Materials*

Nonmagnetic materials cannot be magnetized by any method. Examples: Glass, plastic, wood.

4. *Diamagnetic Materials*

Diamagnetic materials are actually mildly repelled by a magnet. They are rare. Example: Bismuth.

LAWS OF MAGNETISM

1. All magnets have a north pole (N-pole) and a south pole (S-pole) at opposite ends of the material (Fig. 4).
2. Like (similar) poles repel each other and unlike poles attract (Fig. 5).
3. The force of attraction (or repulsion) between two poles is
   a. Directly proportional to the strength of the poles (Fig. 6). Example: The strength of N-pole *A* is 3 units; the strength of S-pole *B* is 6 units.
   Total force between them is $3 \times 6 = 18$.
   b. Inversely proportional to the square of the distance between them.
   Example: The same two poles as above, *A* and *B*, are separated by 3 cm.
   The force between them now is $\frac{18}{3 \times 3} = \frac{18}{9} = 2.$

(A) (B)
S (3) N | S (6) N

(a) Magnets touching each other

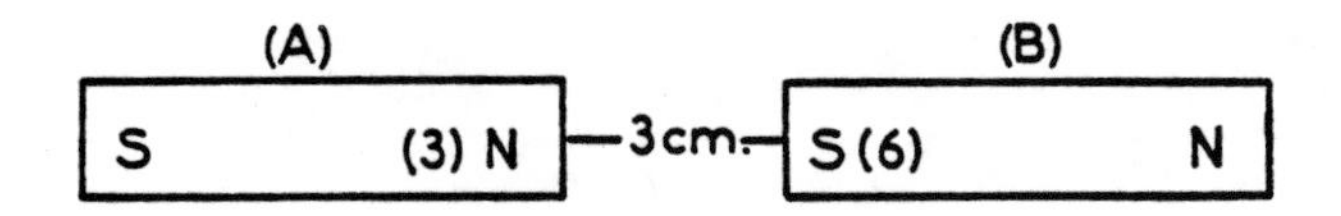

(b) Magnets separated

Figure 6.

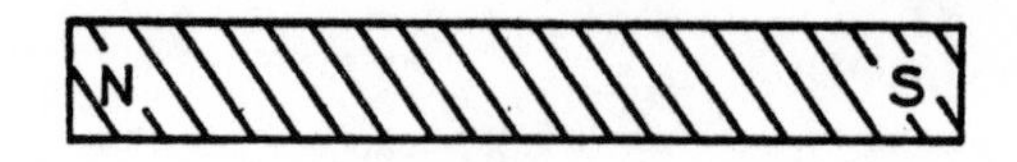

equals

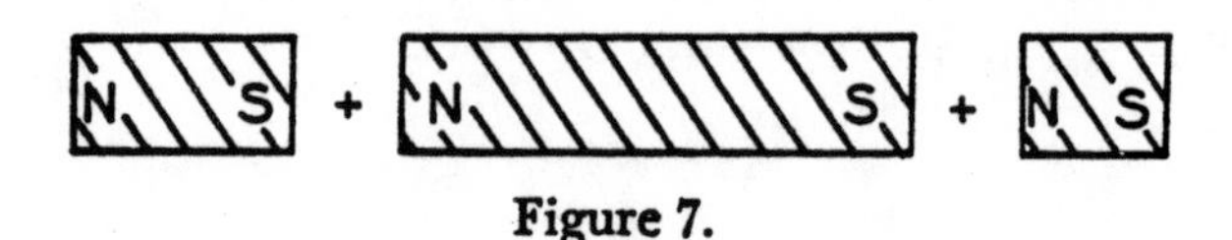

Figure 7.

4. If a magnet is cut into pieces, each piece becomes a magnet in its own right (Fig. 7).

This is logical when the theory of magnetic domains is explained.

THEORY OF MAGNETIC DOMAINS (THE NATURE OF MAGNETISM)

The materials of a magnet are made up of millions of atoms. Each of these atoms is composed of a nucleus and orbiting electrons.

The direction in which the electrons orbit the nucleus is called the spin of the electron. In some elements the electrons all spin in the same direction. These elements can be magnetized. Other elements have electrons which spin in all directions and these cannot be magnetized. The degree to which an element can be

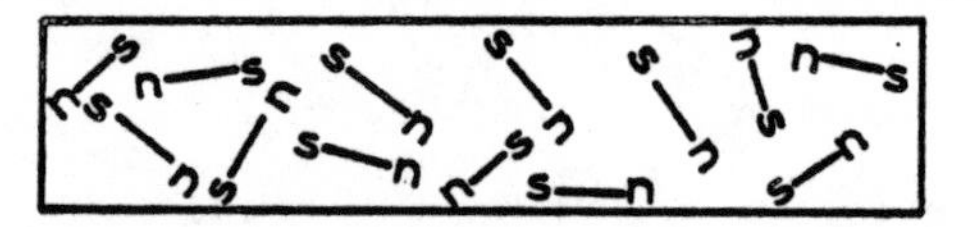

(a) Demagnetized

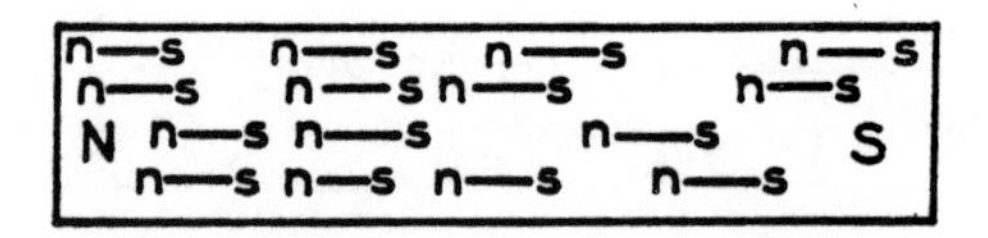

(b) Magnetized

Figure 8. Theory of magnetic domains.

magnetized depends upon the number of its electrons that spin in the same direction.

In a magnetizable material each atom can be said to have a north pole and a south pole. (It is actually easier to visualize each atom as a tiny bar magnet). These "minimagnets" are known as magnetic domains. When a potential magnet is demagnetized, the domains are arranged in a haphazard manner (Fig 8). When a magnetizing force is applied, the magnetic domains are rearranged so that they lie with all the north poles facing in one direction and all the south poles in the opposite direction. (All the electrons are spinning in the same direction.)

MAGNETIC INDUCTION—MAKING A MAGNET

1. *High Permeability Material*

To make a magnet from material with high permeability is easy.

a. *Direct Induction.* Lay the bar of material end to end or side to side with a permanent magnet and the magnetic domains will become aligned in the same direction. The material will have become magnetized. The south pole of the permanent magnet will induce a north pole in the end of material nearest to it. Similarly, the north pole will induce a south pole (Fig. 9).

b. *Stroking.* This is also a process of induction. By stroking

(a) End to end direct induction

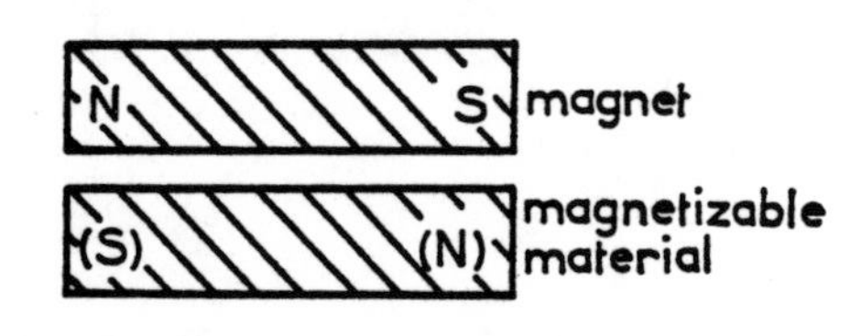

(b) Side by side direct induction

Figure 9. Making a magnet by direct induction.

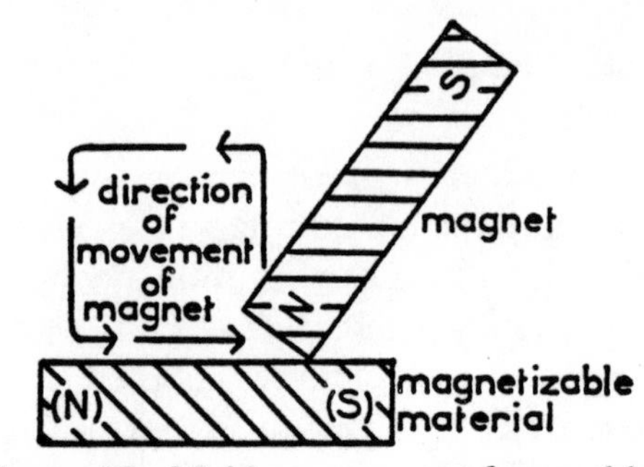

Figure 10. Making a magnet by stroking.

a bar of magnetic material with a permanent magnet the material will become magnetized (Fig. 10).

2. *Low Permeability Material*

To make a magnet from a material with low permeability is difficult. It is necessary to lay the material alongside a permanent magnet and then either hammer or heat the material. This will vibrate the magnetic domains sufficiently to allow them to be realigned. On the other hand, it is just as difficult to demagnetize the material, and this property can be most valuable.

MAGNETIC FIELDS

Around every magnet there is a zone of force known as a magnetic field. The distribution of magnetic force in this field can be

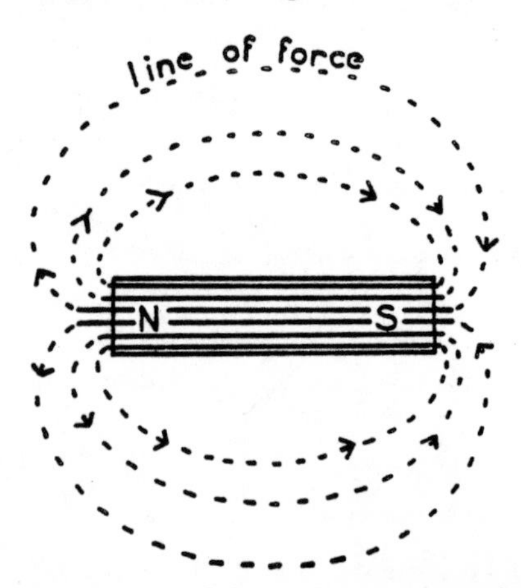

Figure 11. Lines of force in a magnetic field.

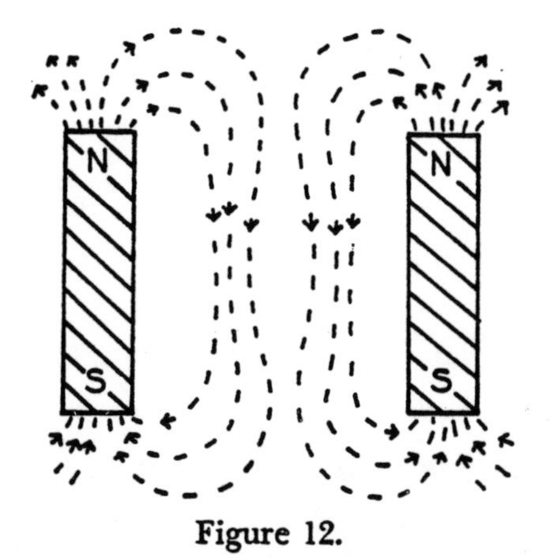

Figure 12.

represented by lines, called lines of force or magnetic flux (Fig 11).

Any high permeability material lying in the magnetic field of a magnet will become magnetized, and attracted to the magnet. Example: A magnet will attract pins and iron filings.

If it were possible to have a solitary north pole moving in the magnetic field, it would move in a certain path: It would be repelled by the north pole of the magnet, travel around a curved path in space and, finally, be attracted back into the magnet at the south pole. This path is known as the direction of a line of force.

The lines of force are said to leave the magnet at the north pole and enter at the south pole.

Lines of force repel each other when they travel in the same direction (Fig. 12).

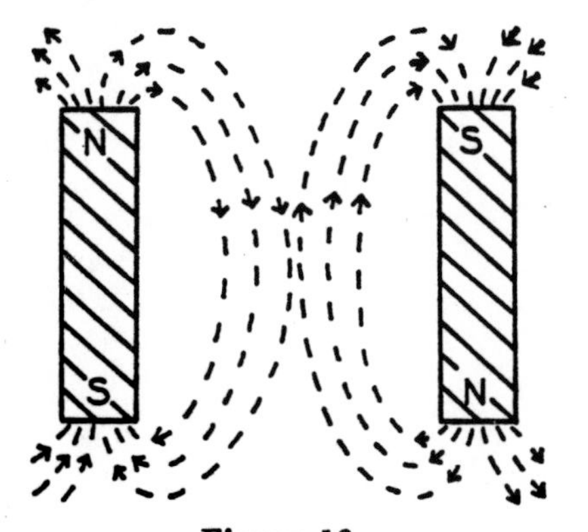

Figure 13.

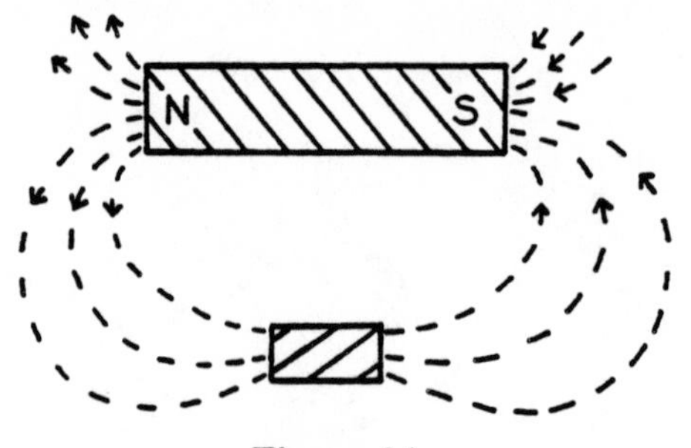

Figure 14.

Lines of force attract each other when they travel in opposite directions (Fig. 13).

Lines of force can be concentrated by magnetic materials, especially those with high permeability (Fig. 14).

The more lines of force there are, the stronger is the magnetic field. Or, conversely, a strong magnetic field will have more lines of force than a weak one.

3 Energy

There are many different kinds of energy: heat, mechanical, electrical, chemical, nuclear, and atomic.

The Law of Conservation of Energy

The law of conservation of energy states that energy can be neither created nor destroyed, only changed. Any form of energy can be changed into any other form. Example: Electrical energy can be changed into heat energy, as in an electric heater.

Einstein discovered that, as well as changing one form of energy into another, it is possible to change energy into mass and vice versa. Thus, mass should really be regarded as a form of energy. He worked out a formula to show the relationship between mass and energy: $E = mc^2$.

where E = energy;

m = mass;

c = the velocity of light (which is the same as the velocity of all electromagnetic radiations).

The equation shows how much energy would be liberated if any given mass were converted into energy. Since c (the speed of light) is such a large number (186,000 miles/sec, or 3×10^{10} cm/sec), you can see that a very large amount of energy would be freed for a relatively small mass being converted. If you look at it from the other direction, it means that a very large amount of energy would be needed to form a very small mass.

Energy is the ability to do work. Expressed as a formula: $W = f \times s$

Where W = work done;
f = force applied (example: how hard you push);
s = the distance through which the force is applied (example: how far you push the object).

Types of Energy

1. *Potential Energy*

Potential energy is the type possessed by a body by virtue of its position. Example: A rock sitting on top of a cliff will possess potential energy because, if it fell to the beach below, by the time it hit someone sunbathing, it would have acquired the energy to cause him damage.

$$\text{potential energy} = m \times g \times h$$

where m = the mass of the object (the rock);
h = the height through which it falls;
g = the acceleration due to gravity.
(g = a constant: 32 ft/sec^2, or 981 cm/sec^2.)

2. *Kinetic Energy*

Kinetic energy is the type acquired by a body when moving. Example: The energy acquired by the rock in falling from the cliff onto the sunbather is the kinetic energy.

$$\text{kinetic energy} = \tfrac{1}{2}mv^2$$

where m = the mass of the object;
v = the velocity with which it is moving when it strikes.

Summary

The potential energy of the rock is the energy it would have if it fell from the cliff top. The kinetic energy is the energy it does have by the time it reaches the bottom of the cliff. The two energies are equal to each other; therefore,

$$\text{potential energy} = \text{kinetic energy}$$

or

$$m \times g \times h = \tfrac{1}{2}mv^2$$

These remarks can be applied to bodies rolling down slopes as well as falling vertically. In this case, however, the h in the formula is not the distance through which the body rolled but the height through which it would have moved had it fallen vertically (Fig. 15).

Potential energy is a useful quantity. Example: The electrical energy stored in a battery is the potential energy of the battery. In this case, reference is made to the difference of potential energy between two points in the battery, the electrodes. This difference is known as the potential difference and its unit is the volt.

The unit of energy which is the most use to us is the electron volt. One electron volt is the kinetic energy acquired by an electron when it is acted on by a potential difference of 1 volt. An electron volt is very small, so it is more usual to speak in terms of million electron volts, written as MeV. One thousand electron volts, one kilo-electron volt, is written as KeV.

Heat

Heat is a very important form of energy in radiology. Almost every form of wasted energy is converted into heat, and in the production of x-rays a great deal of heat is produced.

To get rid of this unwanted heat is a major task and to understand how it is done, it is necessary to know the ways in which heat can be transmitted from one place to another.

1. *Conduction*

The molecules of a substance are in constant motion; they perform a kind of "molecular dance." Conduction is the means by which heat is transmitted through a solid substance, and it uses this movement of the molecules to do it.

As the material gets hotter and the temperature rises the mole-

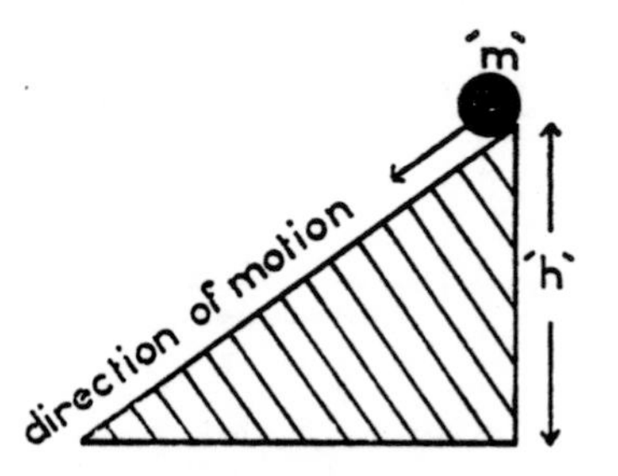

Figure 15. A body rolling down a slope.

cules begin to move faster. Example: If one end of a metal bar is heated, the molecules at that end will begin to vibrate more rapidly. As they speed up they will excite the cooler molecules farther along the bar. These will, in turn, excite the molecules even farther along the bar.

Since this increased motion means a rise in temperature of the substance, the temperature of the bar will gradually rise along its length. The heat is said to have been conducted along the bar. Some materials are better conductors of heat than others. For example, metal is a better conductor of heat than plastic. A material that does not conduct heat very well is called an insulator.

The process of conduction works in solids because their molecules are packed closely enough together to allow "direct" excitation.

2. *Convection*

Convection is the process by which heat is transferred through fluids. A fluid is any substance that flows; this definition covers both liquids and gases. The molecules of a fluid are more widely spaced than those of a solid. The more spaced they are, the more like a gas is the fluid (Fig. 16).

As the molecules of a fluid are heated they spread out, thus occupying more space for the same mass; that is, they become less dense. A substance that is less dense than its surroundings will tend to rise. Thus, as a fluid is heated it starts to rise. As the heated part reaches the top of the vessel in which it is contained the space it used to occupy is taken over by the part of the fluid that has

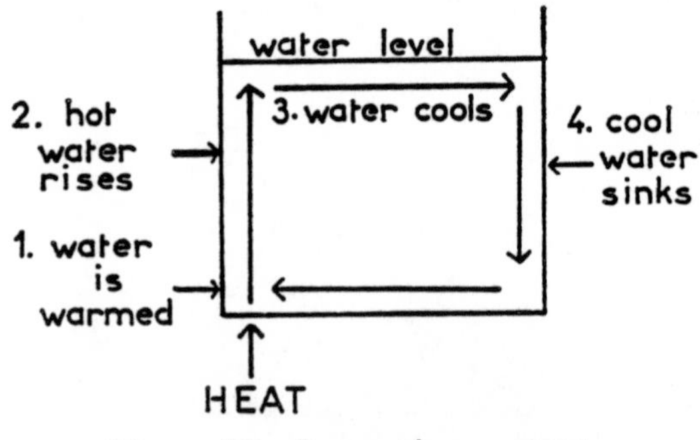

Figure 16. Convection current.

not yet been heated. This process of movement of the fluid on heating is known as a convection current. By this mechanism the heat becomes evenly distributed throughout the fluid.

3. *Radiation*

Radiation is the process by which heat is transmitted across a vacuum. A vacuum has no (or very few) molecules in it. A different way, therefore, must be operative for the transfer of heat.

Heat, as a form of energy, belongs to the class electromagnetic radiation. (This will be explained more fully in a later section.) Electromagnetic radiation travels in waves and can be transmitted through a vacuum. Radiation is, therefore, the transmission of heat as electromagnetic radiation through a vacuum. The heat travels in straight lines and is transferred to any object that it strikes. Example: This is the way heat is transmitted to the earth from the sun.

Ionization

A normal atom is electrically balanced, with the same number of negative charges in orbit (on the electrons) as positive charges on the nucleus (protons). If, for any reason, a negative charge is removed from the atom, it is left with an overall positive charge. The process of removing an electron is known as ionization, and the resulting separate electron and positive atom are known as an ion pair.

The positive atom is called a positive ion, and the electron that has been removed from its orbit is a negative ion. Sometimes the electron becomes attached to another atom, giving this an overall negative charge; this is also called a negative ion.

Ionization can be caused by anything that has the energy to remove an electron from its orbit. Examples: Heat, light (in fact all electromagnetic radiation), alpha and beta particles, concussion. The less energy the ionizing agent possesses the less likely it is to cause ionization.

Electromagnetic Radiation

Electromagnetic radiation is the means by which energy is transferred directly from one place to another; that is, without using any other agency, such as a solid or a fluid.

Electromagnetic Spectrum

Electromagnetic radiation varies from very weak radiation, with hardly any energy, to extremely strong radiation, with a great deal of energy. Electromagnetic radiations are identified, or labeled, either by stating the energy level or the wavelength.

Low energy is found to be associated with long wavelength, and high energy with short wavelength. The various electromagnetic radiations are arranged in order of their energy and are found to form a continuous spectrum, with the upper energy level of one type of radiation running into, and overlapping with, the lower end of the next. Example: The higher energy heat radiations begin to overlap the visible light spectrum in the area known as infrared.

In rising order of their energy levels, here are the main divisions of the electromagnetic spectrum:

Radio waves—lowest energy, longest wavelength.
Infrared.
Visible light.
Ultraviolet light.
X-rays.
Gamma rays.
Cosmic rays—highest energy, shortest wavelength.

Laws of Electromagnetic Radiation

1. Electromagnetic radiations consist of energy. They have no mass and no charge and cannot be deflected by a magnetic or electric field.
2. They travel in straight lines when in free space.
3. They all travel with the same velocity in free space. The velocity of electromagnetic radiation is a constant and is 186,000 miles/sec or 3×10^{10} cm/sec.
4. When they pass through a material, they become attenuated (weakened) because they are partly absorbed by the material. That is, they lose part of their energy to the material.
5. In free space they obey the inverse square law. This states that the intensity of the radiation at any point is inversely

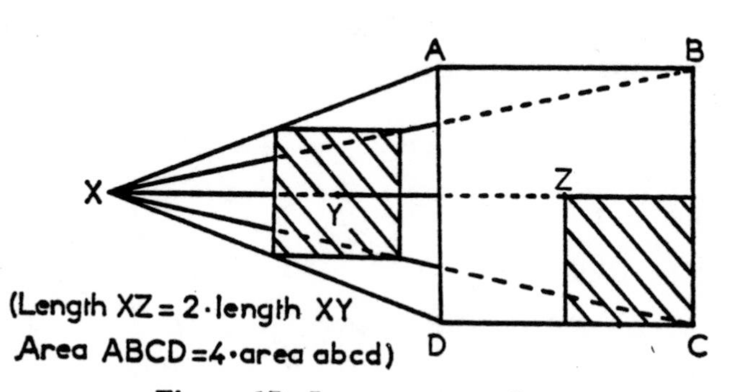

Figure 17. Inverse square law.

proportional to the square of the distance of that point from the source of radiation (Fig. 17).

This means, for example, that if the intensity of a beam of radiation is measured at two points, *A* and *B*, with *B* being twice as far as *A* from the source, the intensity at *B* is one-fourth that of the intensity at *A* and not one half as would be supposed.

If *B* were four times as far away as *A*, then the intensity at *B* would be $\frac{1}{4^2} = \frac{1}{16}$;
if *B* were eight times as far away, then the intensity would be $\frac{1}{8^2} = \frac{1}{64}$;
and so on.

This law can be written as a formula:

$$\frac{I_1}{I_2} = \frac{d_2^2}{d_1^2}$$

where I_1 = the intensity at *A*;
I_2 = the intensity at *B*;
d_2 = the distance *B* from the source;
d_1 = the distance *A* from the source.

Formula for Use by Radiology Students

In radiology it is often required to find what distance will give a certain intensity of x-rays. The inverse square law formula can be easily modified to cover this:

$$d_2^2 = d_1^2 \times \frac{I_1}{I_2}$$

In other words,

$$(\text{the new distance})^2 = (\text{old distance})^2 \times \frac{\text{old intensity}}{\text{new intensity}}$$

Formula for Use by Radiotherapy Students

The most frequent use of the inverse square law in radiotherapy is to find the new intensity (or output) at an increased or decreased treatment distance. For this the formula can also be rearranged:

$$I_2 = I_1 \times \frac{d_1^2}{d_2^2}$$

or

$$\text{new output} = \text{Old output} \times \frac{(\text{Old distance})^2}{(\text{New distance})^2}$$

Example: In practice this means that if an ssd (source to skin distance) on the machine has been altered, the new output can be found by applying the formula:
Old output = 80 rads/min; new output = ?;
Old ssd = 80 cm; new ssd = 100 cm.

$$\text{New output} = 80 \times \frac{80^2}{100^2} = 51.2 \text{ rads/min.}$$

6. Electromagnetic radiations transfer energy in "bundles." These are called photons or quanta. Electromagnetic radiations also travel with a wavelike motion. The basis for saying that they travel in bundles and in waves is that some of their properties can be explained by saying they travel as waves and some by saying that they travel in quanta. The easiest way to resolve the dilemma is to imagine that they do indeed travel in small bursts of energy (the quanta) but that these quanta follow a wavelike path.

   a. *The Wave Theory.* When you throw a stone in a pond, the disturbance it causes travels outward in waves. Similarly, when you agitate a skipping rope up and down, the waves move along the rope. Although the waves move up and down, the actual direction of movement is forward, away from the source. These are called transverse waves; electromagnetic waves travel in this manner. In other words, the fluctuation is at right angles to the direction of motion.

Waves have certain features associated with them.

i. *Wavelength.* This is the distance from a point on one wave to the same point on the next wave. For example, the distance from one peak to the next, or one trough to the next. The shorter the wavelength the higher the energy of the radiation (Fig. 18).

ii. *Frequency.* This is the number of waves that occur per second. The higher the frequency the higher the energy. This is logical because the higher energy wave has a shorter wavelength and would naturally occur more times in a second.

iii. *Velocity.* This is the distance traveled per second by the wave.

iv. *Amplitude.* This is the height of the wave from the baseline to the crest (or the trough) and is also, therefore, equal to half the distance between the crest and the trough. Wavelength, frequency, and velocity are related to each other in a simple way:

velocity = wavelength × frequency

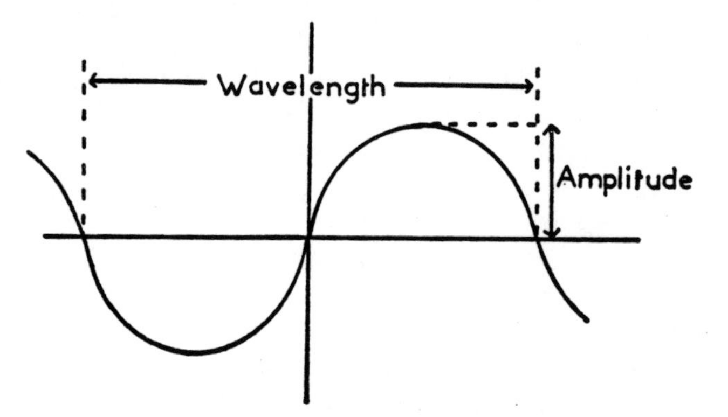

Figure 18. Wavelength and amplitude.

Since the velocity is a constant (186,000 miles/sec), this means that you can say that the wavelength is inversely proportional to the frequency (inverse just means upside down). That means that the longer the wavelength, the less is the frequency, and vice versa.

b. *Quantum (or Photon) Theory.* Although the radiation follows a wavelike path, it is not emitted in a continuous stream but in bundles of radiation, called photons or quanta (the singular of quanta is quantum). These photons are emitted a bit like peas from a peashooter.

Connection Between the Two Theories. The wave theory and the quantum theory can be linked together in a simple relationship.

E (the energy in a photon) = frequency × Planck's constant (Planck's constant is just a number). We already know that frequency $= \frac{\text{speed of light}}{\text{wavelength}}$ (from the formula velocity = wavelength × frequency). So for frequency we can substitute $\frac{\text{"speed of light"}}{\text{wavelength}}$ and then the formula reads:

$$\text{energy (in photon)} = \text{Planck's constant} \times \frac{\text{speed of light}}{\text{wavelength}}$$

Ionizing Radiations

The ionizing radiations with which we are concerned in radiology, and, particularly, in radiotherapy, are alpha particles (alpha rays), beta particles (beta rays), neutrons, x-rays, and gamma rays.

Alpha rays, beta rays, and neutrons are particles; that is, they have mass. In addition alpha and beta particles are electrically charged. X-rays and gamma rays are electromagnetic radiation and have no mass and no charge.

Specific Ionization

The amount of ionization (that is "atomic damage") produced in a certain distance is called the specific ionization. Alpha particles have a double positive charge and are therefore deviated from their track many times within a very short distance, thus giving up their energy relatively quickly. Because an alpha particle causes much ionization in a short distance, it is said to have a high specific ionization. It therefore follows that a high specific ionization indicates low energy radiation.

Beta particles are much smaller and carry only a single, negative charge. They are not deviated so many times in a similar distance, that is, they do not cause so much ionization. The specific ionization of a beta particle is thus less than that of an alpha particle.

X-rays and gamma rays have neither mass nor charge and therefore cause even less ionization per unit length than either the alpha or beta particle. X-rays and gamma rays have the smallest value of all for specific ionization and therefore the greatest penetrating power.

Neutrons

Recently experiments have been carried out using neutrons for radiotherapy treatment. The theory of their use in treating tumors is as follows: Tumors are often structures lacking in oxygen. Any tissue which is deficient in oxygen will not be affected as much by radiation as a normally oxygenated one. Thus oxygen-lacking tumors tend to be radioresistant.

Physicists have discovered that neutrons with an energy range of about 4 MeV appear to have the same damaging effect on tissues irrespective of whether there is oxygen present or not. This work is only in the experimental stage. For treatment purposes neutrons can be produced in equipment very similar to an x-ray tube. This consists of (a) a discharge tube containing deuterium at low pressure, (b) a high frequency electric field passed through this to produce deuterons, and (c) a voltage of 150 kV to accelerate the deuterons onto a tritium target.

Direct and Indirect Ionization

Alpha and beta particles produce most of their ionization directly. That is, they remove electrons from their orbits themselves. Gamma rays, x-rays, and neutrons produce most of their ionization indirectly. That is, most of the ionization attributable to them is actually produced secondarily by the electrons which they originally removed from orbit doing further damage.

4 Electricity

There are two types of electricity: (a) *electrostatic* which deals with static electricity, and (b) *electrodynamic* (or current electricity) which deals with moving electric charges.

Electrostatics

Electrostatic electrification is the same process as ionization. That is, electrons are removed from atoms and either remain free or become attached to other, neutral atoms. Positive and negative ions are formed and are called positive and negative charges.

There are two kinds of material associated with electricity: (a) *conductors,* which allow the passage of electric charges and currents, and (b) *insulators,* which prevent the passage of electricity.

There are two kinds of electrostatic charge: (a) *negative charge,* which is formed either of a single electron removed from orbit or of an atom with a surplus electron attached, and (b) *positive charge,* which is formed of an atom with an electron deficiency.

Methods of Electrification

There are three methods of producing a charge of static electricity.

1. *Friction*

If one body is rubbed with another, electrons are removed from one, giving it a positive charge, and added to the other, giving it a negative charge. Example: If glass is rubbed with silk, the silk picks up electrons from the glass, giving it a negative charge and leaving the glass with a positive charge.

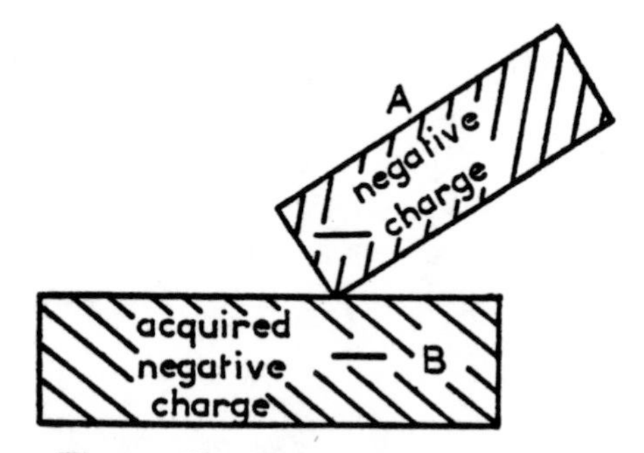

Figure 19. Charging by contact.

2. *Contact*

If an uncharged body is touched by one which has been charged, then the uncharged body will become charged (Fig. 19). If the charging body, *A,* is negative (surplus electrons) when it touches the uncharged body, *B,* then *A* will share its surplus electrons and *B* will also become negatively charged. In other words, when a body is charged by direct contact, the charge acquired is the same as that on the charging body. If the charging body is positively charged (lack of electrons), the uncharged body would share its electrons with the deficient body and so leave them both with an overall deficiency and consequent positive charge.

3. *Induction*

Around each charged body is an area of force, similar to a magnetic field, called an electrostatic field. If a charged body, *A,* is brought near an uncharged body, *B,* then a charge will be induced on *B* (Fig. 20). If *A* has a negative charge, the electrostatic

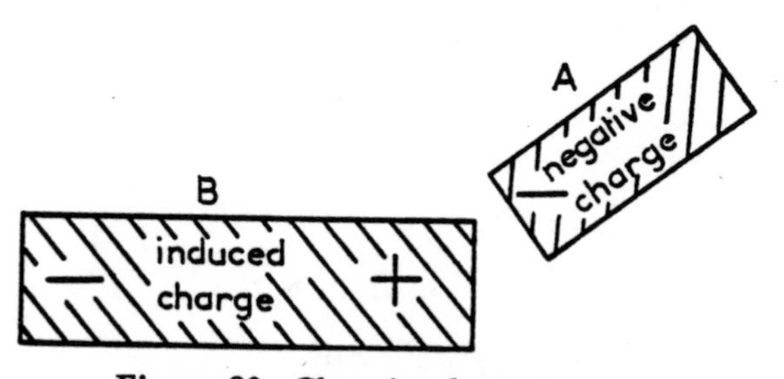

Figure 20. Charging by induction.

field around it will repel the electrons at the near end (because like charges repel) to the far end, giving the near end a positive charge and the far end a negative charge. Thus the charge induced by a charged body is opposite to that on the charging body. This is the opposite to the effect produced when charging a body by contact. The charge induced will disappear when the charging influence is removed.

Making the Induced Charge Permanent

The charge may be made permanent by grounding the negative end of the body being charged (*B*). All the surplus electrons at the negative end will flow to ground (see next section). When the ground connection is removed, the remaining electrons will spread out, and since there is now an overall deficiency of electrons, the body will be permanently positively charged (Fig. 21).

Ground

The earth (ground) is regarded as a huge reservoir of electrons. If a negative charge is connected to ground, all the surplus electrons will flow to the reservoir and return the charged body to a neutral state. If a positively charged body is connected to ground, electrons will flow from ground to the body to neutralize the charge on it.

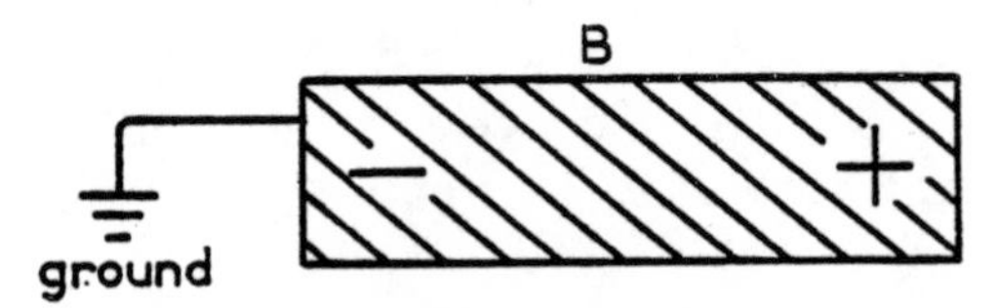

(a) Body Grounded

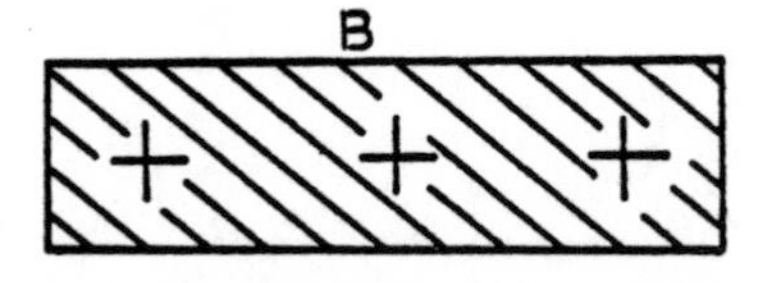

(b) Body Positively Charged

Figure 21. Making the charge permanent.

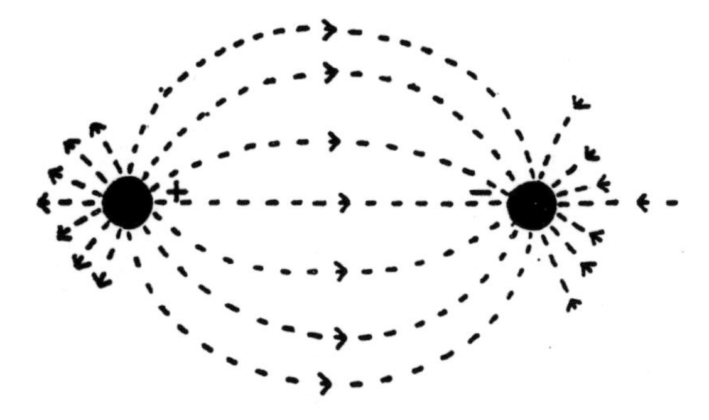

Figure 22a. Unlike charges attract.

Laws of Electrostatics

1. Like charges repel each other and unlike charges attract (Figs. 22a and 22b). This is the same as the law of magnetism dealing with poles. The electrostatic field has lines of force, just as the magnetic field does. The positive charge can be likened to a north pole and the negative charge to a south pole. The lines of electrostatic force leave the positive pole and enter at the negative pole.
2. The electrostatic force between two charges is (a) directly proportional to the product of their magnitudes, and (b) inversely propotional to the square of the distance between them. Example: Two charges located side by side have magnitudes of 3 and 6. The force between them is $3 \times 6 = 18$. If they are moved 3 cm apart, the force between them is now: $\frac{3 \times 6}{3^2} = \frac{18}{9} = 2$.
3. Electric charges reside only on the outside of conductors. If,

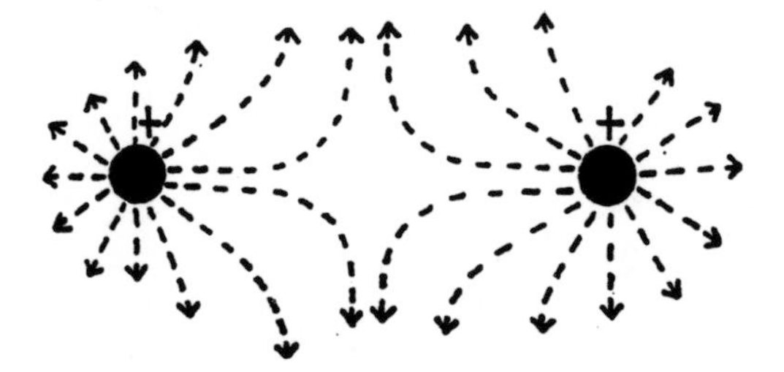

Figure 22b. Like charges repel.

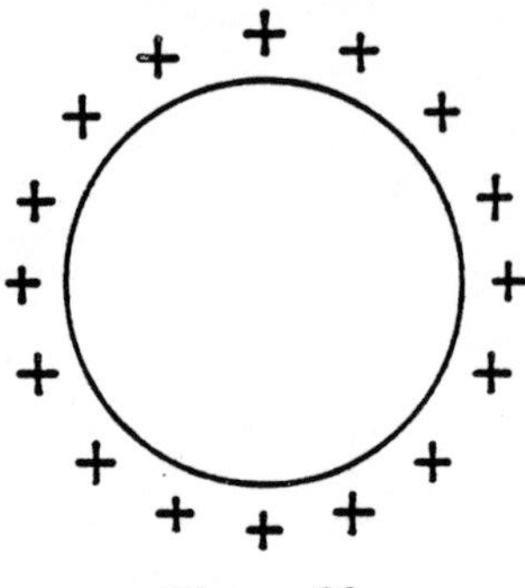

Figure 23.

say, a hollow sphere (ball) is charged, all of the charge will be found to be on the outside of the sphere and the inside will be uncharged (Fig. 23). This is due to the fact that like charges repel and will push as far apart from each other as possible, thus making it impossible for them to reside next to each other on the inside of the sphere.

4. Charges on a curved surface are concentrated around the part of greatest curvature (Fig. 24). The charge concentrated on a pinpoint may be so great that it starts to leak away.
5. Only negative charges can move in a solid conductor. This is due to the fact that the atoms of a solid conductor are so closely packed together that only negative charges in the form of electrons are small enough to move among them.

Electroscope

An electroscope is a device used to detect electric charges. It

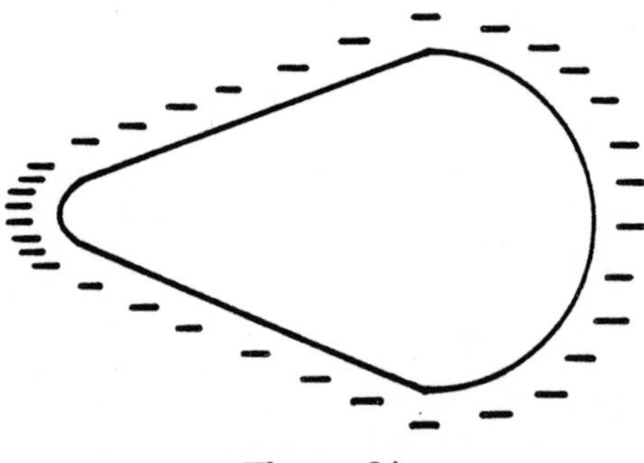

Figure 24.

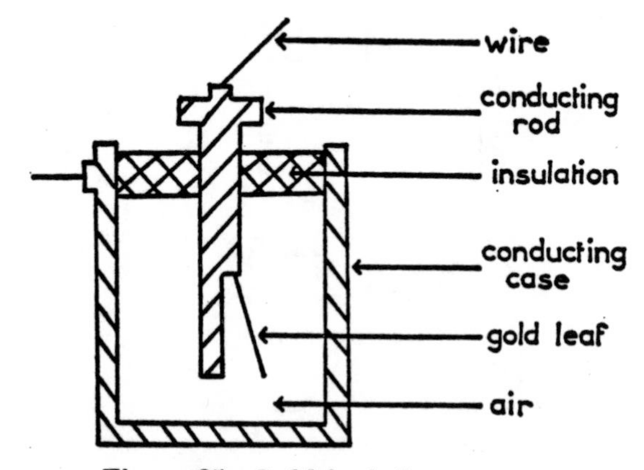

Figure 25. Gold leaf electroscope.

is a primitive instrument and is not now used in any practical way, just for explanation and demonstration.

When the metal rod is charged, the gold leaves will acquire the same charge as the rod and as each other (Fig. 25). Being similarly charged and also very light in weight, the gold leaves will push away from each other.

Charging an Electroscope

There are two ways to charge an electroscope.

1. *Contact*

Contact will produce a similar charge to the charging body. If a charged body touches the metal knob, a similar charge will be imparted to the electroscope (Fig. 26).

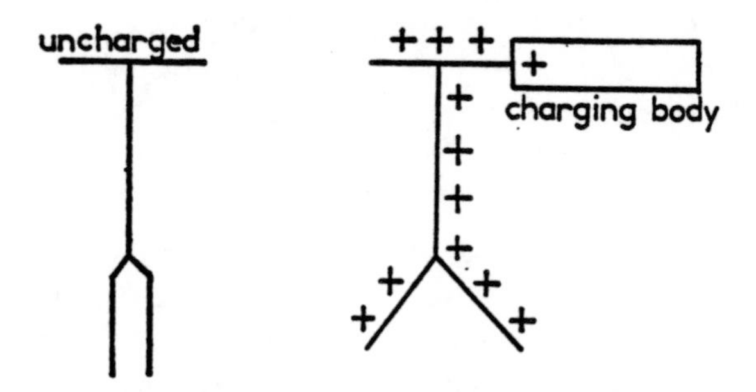

Figure 26. Charging an electroscope by contact.

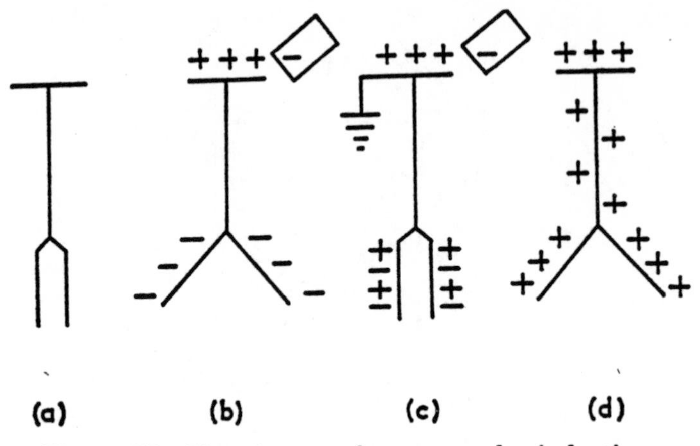

Figure 27. Charging an electroscope by induction.

2. *Induction*

Induction will produce an opposite charge on the electroscope to that on the charging body (Fig. 27). To make the charge on the electroscope permanent when using the induction method, it is necessary to ground the metal knob of the electroscope while the charging influence is still present and then to remove both ground and charger.

The Electroscope as a Detector of X-rays

When x-rays pass through air, they produce ionization. When a charged electroscope is placed in air which is being ionized, some of the ions produced by the x-rays neutralize the charge on the electroscope and cause the gold leaves to fall (become less separated). This happens because as the charge on the electroscope falls so does the repulsion of the gold leaves for each other. The amount of x-rays that have passed can be measured by the degree that the gold leaves have fallen.

Static Discharge

When the charge on two oppositely charged bodies becomes very great, the substance between the two bodies cannot keep the charges separated and a spark jumps from the negatively charged body to the positively charged one. The spark consists of electrons

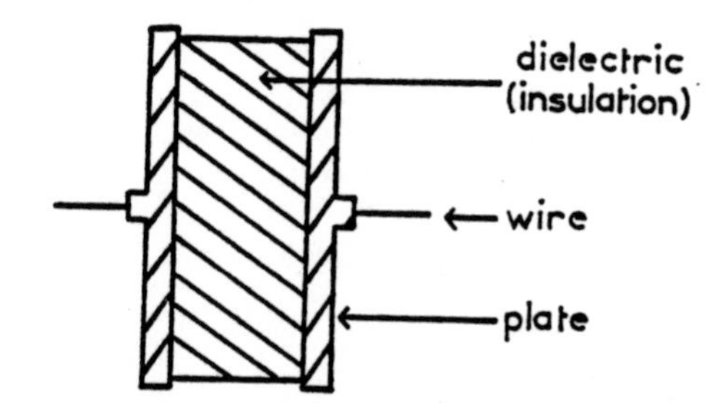

Figure 28. Construction of a capacitor.

moving from negative to positive, in one big burst, to neutralize the positive charge. The negatively charged body is said to be at a higher negative potential than the positively charged one.

Capacitors (Condensers)

A condenser is a means of storing static electricity. When a conducting body is charged, the charge spreads out over the whole surface of that body.

Construction of a Capacitor

A basic capacitor consists of two parallel plates separated and insulated from each other (Fig. 28). This means that there is no direct electrical connection between the two plates; therefore, there can be no flow of electricity between them. This is called a parallel plate capacitor. The insulation between the plates is called the dielectric.

If a capacitor is connected in circuit with a battery, electrons pass from the negative terminal of the battery to the one plate of the capacitor; this gives it a negative charge. Electrons pass from the other plate to the positive terminal of the battery; this gives that plate a positive charge.

We thus have a capacitor with one plate charged up negatively in respect to the other and no electrical connection between the plates (Fig. 29). If the battery is now removed and no connection is made between the plates, the charge will remain stored in the capacitor.

If, when the charge is needed to do work, a connection is made between the two plates, the surplus electrons on the negative plate

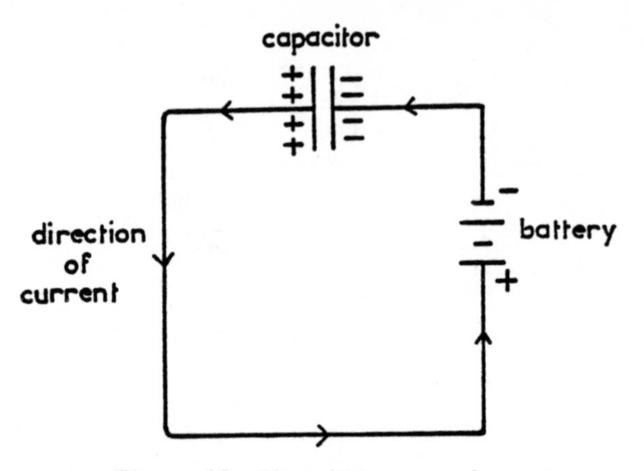

Figure 29. Charging a capacitor.

will move around the connection to even out the charge on the positive plate, that is, to neutralize it. This movement of electrons constitutes an electric current (Fig. 30). The current from a capacitor will flow in the opposite direction to which it would have flowed had it been used directly from the battery.

The Capacity of a Capacitor (Capacitance)

Capacitance is the amount of electricity that can be stored by a particular capacitor. It is measured in farads. A farad is the amount of electricity, in coulombs, which is stored for each volt

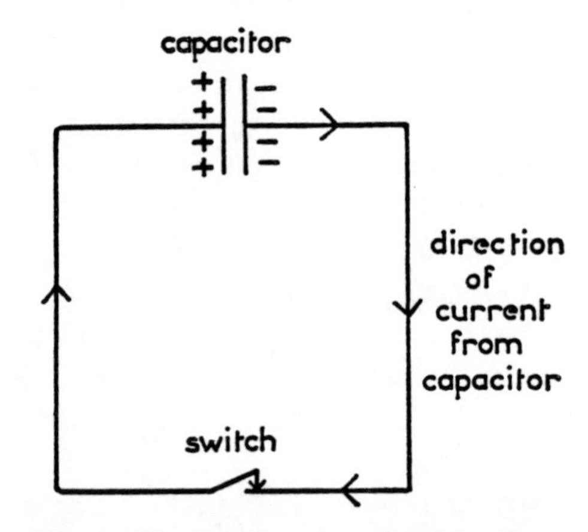

Figure 30. Discharging the capacitor.

of potential difference that is applied to the capacitor. A coulomb is the amount of electricity which, if it flowed for one second in an ionic solution, would deposit a standard amount of metal from that solution. Capacitance depends up on three things.

1. It is directly proportional to the area of the plates. The bigger the plates, the larger the capacitance, that is, the more charge it can hold.
2. It is inversely proportional to the distance apart of the plate. The farther apart, the smaller the capacitance.
3. It is directly proportional to the dielectric constant. Dielectric is the name given to the insulator between the plates. The better the insulation, the more charge can be held by the plates. The dielectric constant tells you how efficient the dielectric is as an insulator. Example: The dielectric constant of air is 1; wax paper is 2, and glass is 7. This means that wax paper is a better insulator than air and glass is better than either of them. The capacitance will be much increased by placing glass between the plate instead of air.

Electrodynamics

Electrodynamics is the study of current electricity or moving charges. An electric current is a flow of charged particles. Electric current will flow under the following circumstances.

1. *In a Solid Conductor*

The electric current here consists of a flow of electrons only. The electrons on the outer shell of the atoms are very often only loosely bound and can be pushed along from one atom to the next. Imagine electrons entering a pipe at one end and leaving at the other. An electric current moves from a point where there is an excess of electrons (a high negative potential) to a point where there is a deficiency of electrons (a low negative potential).

Although the current is described as a flow of electrons, the electrons do not just rush through the conductor from one end to the other. What happens is that they "bump into" one another and so cause a general shift from one end to the other. An electron enters at the high negative potential end of the conductor, pushes the next electron along a little in the direction which it wants

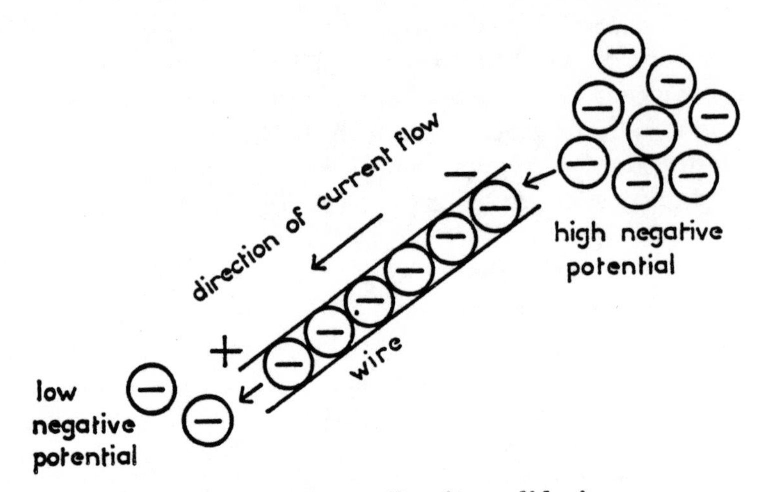

Figure 31. Current flow in a solid wire.

to go, this in turn pushes the next, and so on. Eventually an electron emerges at the low negative potential end (Fig. 31). The net result is that of an electron having traveled very rapidly from one end of the conductor to the other, whereas in actual fact each electron has moved only a very small distance indeed.

The current will continue to flow as long as one end of the conductor is at a higher negative potential than the other, in other words, as long as one end has more electrons than the other. As soon as each end of the conductor has the same number of electrons the current, or movement of electrons, will stop. If, on the other hand, the electrons are removed as soon as they arrive at the low negative potential end and returned to the high negative potential end, then the current will keep flowing.

2. *In an Ionic Solution*

When certain compounds, called salts, are dissolved in water, they split into their component parts in the form of charged particles called ions. A solution of a salt is therefore called an ionic solution. Example: Sodium chloride (NaCl) splits to form a positive sodium ion (Na^+) and a negative chloride ion (Cl^-). The sodium atom has lost an electron to the chlorine atom.

If two electrodes from a battery are now dipped into the solu-

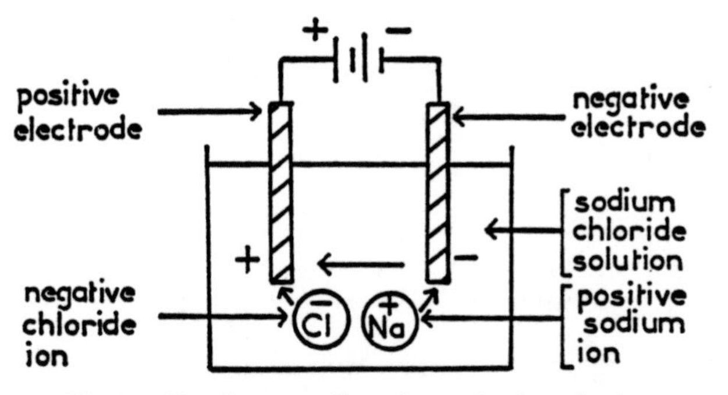

Figure 32. Current flow in an ionic solution.

tion, the positive sodium ion moves toward the negative electrode and the negative chloride ion moves toward the positive electrode. The net result is that there is a movement of electrons from the negative electrode to the positive and this constitutes an electric current (Fig. 32).

3. *In a Gas*

Two oppositely charged electrodes placed in a gas will cause behavior similar to that in an ionic solution. When a potential difference is applied across the gas between the electrodes, that is, when one of the electrodes is made negative with respect to the other, the gas molecules will become ionized. The positive ions will move toward the negative electrode and the negative ions will move toward the positive. The net result will again be one of moving electrons from a region of high negative potential to one of low negative potential, in other words, a current has been passed. When some ionizing agency, such as x-rays, has previously been passed through the gas, there will be an increased number of ionized gas molecules present, and thus the passage of the current will be made easier. This fact can be used in the measurement of x-rays.

4. *In a Vacuum*

If two electrodes are placed in a vacuum and a potential difference is applied across them, normally the vacuum will act as a very efficient insulator and prevent the passage of the electrons, that is, the passage of the current. If, however, the potential dif-

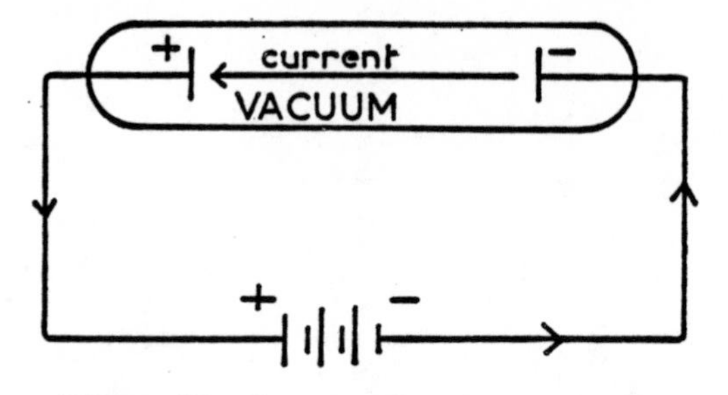

Figure 33. Current flow in a vacuum.

ference across the electrodes is great enough; that is, if there is a sufficiently large number of electrons built up on the negative electrode, the insulatory property of the vacuum will be overcome and a current will flow between the electrodes (Fig. 33). This is the process that occurs in an x-ray tube.

Sources of Electric Current

Current electricity is a form of energy and can be produced only by converting another form of energy. There are two main ways of doing this: (a) Chemical energy is changed to electrical energy, as in a battery. (b) Mechanical energy is changed to electrical energy, as in a generator.

The Battery

A battery actually consists of a collection, or battery, of cells, each of which converts chemical energy to electrical energy. The electricity produced is in the form of direct current.

There are two types of batteries.

1. *Dry Cell*

The dry cell is constructed as shown in Figure 34. Although called "dry," it is actually wet, as its chemicals are in the form of a paste. The chemical paste contains ammonium chloride, manganese dioxide, cellulose, and water. The carbon rod is not in contact with the zinc can. The chemicals in the paste react with the zinc of the can and the carbon of the rod, and the energy produced in the reaction is converted to electrical energy. A potential difference is produced between the electrodes (rod and can).

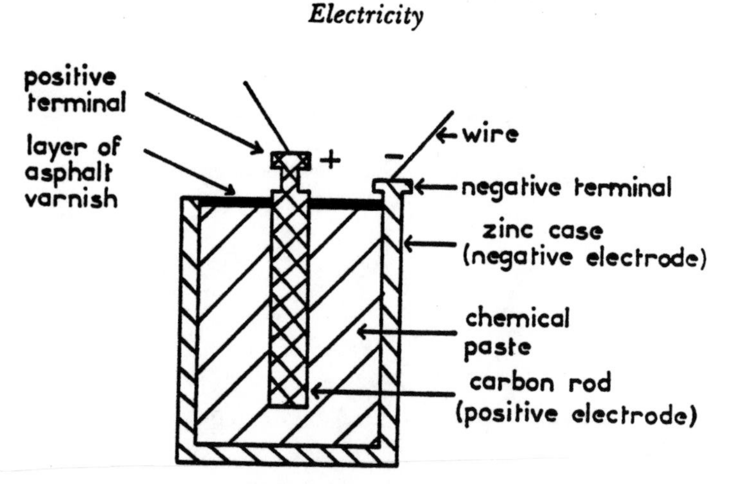

Figure 34. Dry cell.

2. *Wet Cell*

The lead and lead oxide electrodes react chemically with the sulphuric acid and create a potential difference between them. This is used as a source of electricity (Fig. 35).

Electric Circuits (Schematics)

Electric circuits can be drawn in plan form. Each component of the circuit has its own symbol. Example: A simple circuit diagram might look something like the one in Figure 37.

Current would not flow in the circuit shown in Figure 37, because the switch is open and the circuit is not complete. This is called open circuit. When the switch is closed the current will flow. This is called closed or complete circuit.

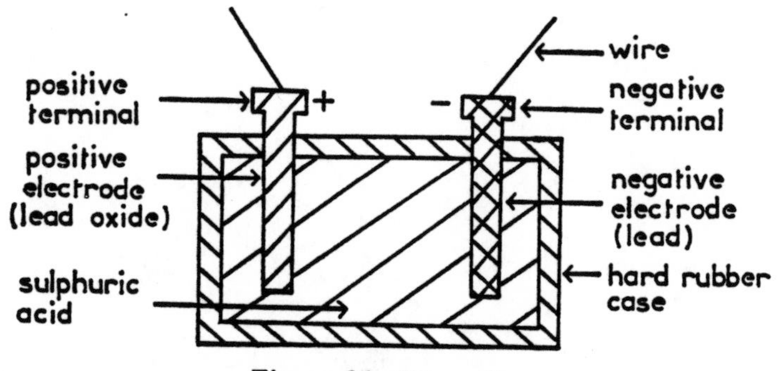

Figure 35. Wet cell.

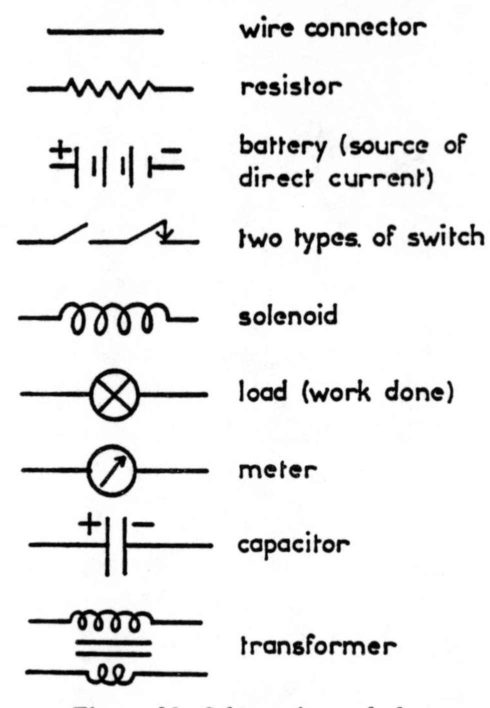

Figure 36. Schematic symbols.

Important Note: An open circuit can have a potential difference (voltage) applied to it even though the current will not flow. The "build up" of electrons is there, but the "evening out" process cannot be started until the pathway (circuit) is complete.

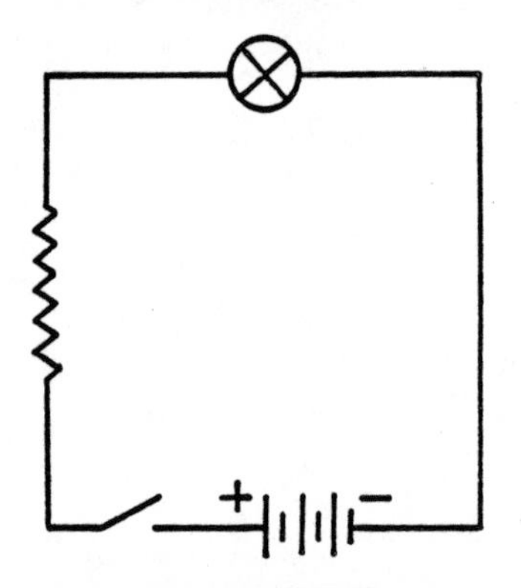

Figure 37. Simple schematic.

There are two types of current: (a) direct current and (b) alternating current.

Direct Current (d.c.)—Factors Involved

1. *Potential Difference (P.D.)*

Potential difference is the difference between the high negative potential and the low negative potential; that is, the difference between the number of electrons at the point of high negative potential and at the low negative potential. The unit of potential difference is the volt. One volt is the potential difference that will cause a current of 1 ampere to flow against a resistance of 1 ohm.

Another name for potential difference is electromotive force (e.m.f.). Potential difference is supplied by a battery or a generator. In simple terms the potential difference is the pushing power of electricity.

2. *Current Strength*

Current strength is the amount of electricity flowing past a certain point in the circuit in one second. The unit of current strength is the ampere. One ampere is a quantity, 1 coulomb, of electricity flowing per second. One coulomb is the amount of electricity required to deposit 0.001118 gm of silver, from an ionic solution of silver nitrate, per second.

It does this by the process described in the section headed "The Passage of an Electric Current Through an Ionic Solution." The positive silver ions move to the negative electrode and become attached to it, forming a deposit of silver on the electrode. This is how electroplating is done. (See p. 44)

3. *Resistance*

The fact that electric current has to move through something, usually a wire known as the conductor, means that there will be a certain amount of opposition to the current. This opposition is called the resistance. The unit of resistance is the ohm. An ohm is the resistance to current that would be offered by a certain standard column of mercury.

Each circuit will offer a built in (inherent) resistance to the current because of the wires through which the current flows. Extra resistance can be added to the circuit as a means of reducing the current. These extra resistances usually take the form of coils of wire. Resistance depends on four factors:

a. *Material.* Different materials offer different amounts of resistance. Conductors offer less resistance than insulators.
b. *Length.* The resistance is directly proportional to the length of the conductor. The longer the conductor, the higher the resistance.
c. *Cross Section.* Resistance is inversely proportional to the cross section of the conductor. A wider conductor offers less resistance than a narrow one. (It helps to think of the conductor as a pipe and the current as water flowing through it. A wide pipe will offer less resistance to the water flowing through it than will a narrow one.)
d. *Temperature.* With metallic conductors, for example a copper wire, the resistance is directly proportional to the temperature. The higher the temperature, the greater the resistance.

Ohm's Law

There is a simple relationship between potential difference (voltage), current, and resistance:

$$\text{potential difference} = \text{current} \times \text{resistance}$$

This relationship is known as Ohm's law. It is usually written symbolically as: $V = IR$

where V = the potential difference (in volts);
I = the current (in amperes);
R = the resistance (in ohms).

Example: If the current is 4 amp and the resistance is 5 ohms, find the potential difference.

Since $V = IR$,
Then $V = (4 \times 5)$ volts
$= 20$ volts.

It is just as easy to find a value for the current or resistance from this formula, provided that the other two values are provided.

Power

Electricity is a form of energy and is therefore able to perform work. Power is the amount of work that an electric current can do per second. This can be written as a formula:

$$\text{power} = \text{current} \times \text{voltage}$$

This is also written as $P = IV$. This formula is often called the power formula. The most common unit of power is the watt. Another, most useful, unit of power is the horsepower. One horsepower is the equivalent of 746 watts.

Heat Loss

Electrical power is often lost in the form of heat. The amount of power lost as heat can be calculated: We are told that $P = IV$ (the power formula). We are also told that $V = IR$ (Ohm's law). So we can substitute for V in the power formula, which now becomes $P = I(IR)$ or $P = I^2R$.

I^2R is the amount of power lost as heat. From this formula we can see two things:

1. The power lost (that is, the heat given off) is directly proportional to the resistance. This means that the greater the resistance in a circuit, the more will be the power lost as heat. Reduce the resistance and the power loss will be reduced.
2. The power lost is proportional to the square of the current. This means that for a large alteration in the current strength, there will be only a small alteration in the power loss. There

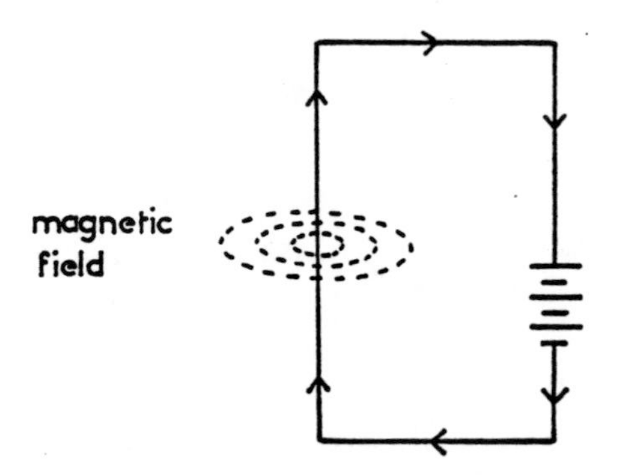

Figure 38. Magnetic field around a current-carrying wire.

can be quite large variations in power supply to the equipment without too much alteration in the power loss.

Electromagnetism

When a current is passed through a wire (conductor) a magnetic field appears around the wire (Fig. 38).

Left-Hand-Thumb Rule

An easy way to discover the direction of the magnetic field produced by a current carrying wire is given by the left-hand-thumb rule. If the wire is grasped by the left hand with the thumb pointing in the direction in which the current is flowing in the wire, then the direction in which the fingers are coiled around the wire shows the direction of the magnetic field.

Electromagnet

If the above wire is coiled into the shape of a spring (this shape is called a helix), the magnetic field then produced by the current flowing behaves as if the helix were a bar magnet (Fig. 39). A helix which has a current flowing through it is called a solenoid.

If the left-hand-thumb rule is now applied to each turn of the wire, the direction of the magnetic field in the coil can be found. An easier way to find the direction of the magnetic field is shown in Figure 40.

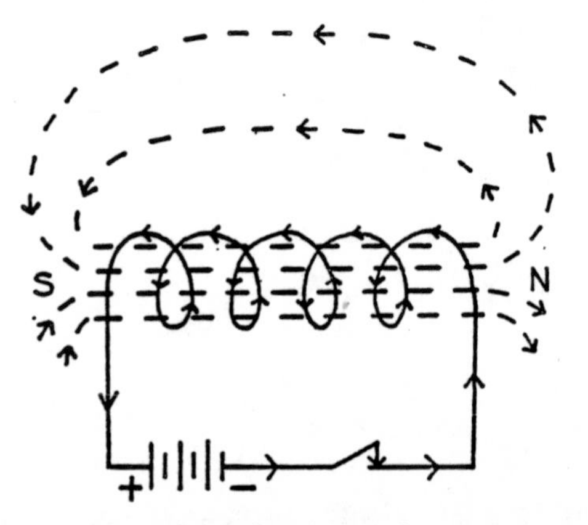

Figure 39. Principle of the electromagnet.

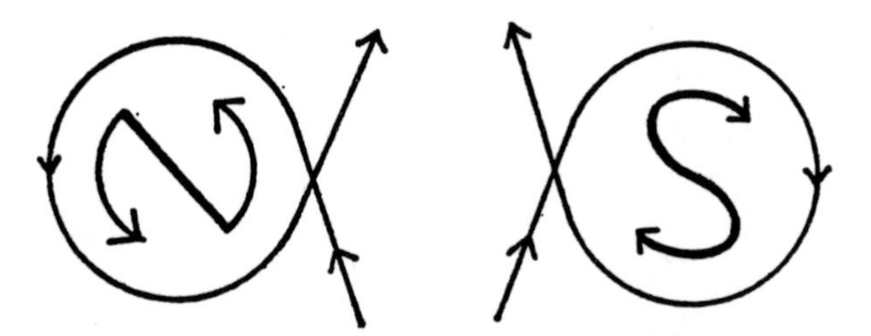

Figure 40. (Imagine you are looking end-on at the solenoid.)

If a magnetic material (ferromagnetic) is placed along the center of the solenoid, the magnetic field becomes concentrated. This bar of magnetic material is called the core of the electromagnet. If the core is made of material of high permeability and low retentivity, such as soft iron, this forms an arrangement whereby a magnet can be produced by passing a current through a solenoid. The effect would of course still occur if the core was omitted, but the presence of the core greatly enhances the magnetic effect.

Electromagnetic Induction

A current flowing through a wire is able to produce a magnetic field. Conversely, a magnetic field surrounding a wire can produce an electric current *provided* that the magnetic field is not steady but constantly changing. A steady magnetic field is not able to produce a current in a wire.

Experimentally, for demonstration purposes, a changing magnetic field can be produced by moving a permanent magnet rapidly in and out of the center of a solenoid. This is illustrated by Figure 41. As the magnet is pushed into the center of the

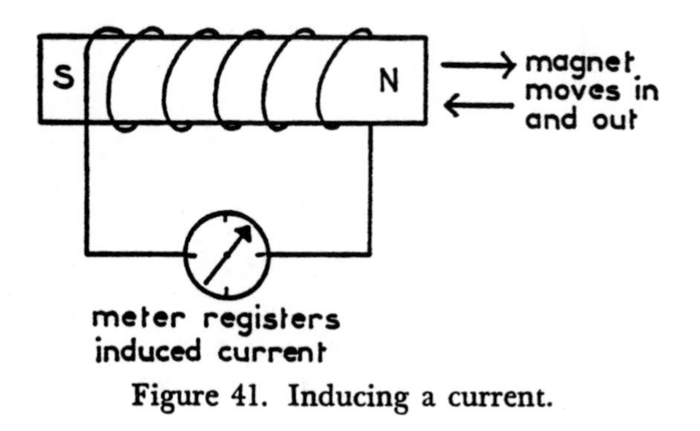

Figure 41. Inducing a current.

solenoid the magnetic field around the solenoid will grow rapidly from zero to a maximum. This constitutes a changing magnetic field and will induce a current to flow in the solenoid. The measuring instrument will show a deflection of the needle in one direction. As the magnet is pulled out from the solenoid the magnetic field will fall from a maximum to zero and, as the magnetic effect has been reversed, the direction of the induced current will be reversed. The needle of the meter will then show a deflection in the opposite direction. The process of producing an electric current by using a changing magnetic field is called electromagnetic induction.

Note: The changing magnetic field actually induces an e.m.f. in the conductor. This e.m.f. will cause a current to flow only when the circuit is complete.

The magnitude of the induced e.m.f. depends on four factors:

1. *The speed* at which the magnetic field cuts the axis of the wire. The faster the magnet is moved in and out of the center of the solenoid the greater will be the induced e.m.f.
2. *The strength* of the inducing magnetic field. A stronger magnet, with more lines of magnetic flux in its field, will induce a greater e.m.f.
3. *The angle* at which the magnetic field is cut by the conductor. The nearer this angle is to 90° (a right angle), the greater the induced e.m.f. This is due to the fact that 90° is the angle at which most lines of flux are cut, in the shortest time.
4. *The number of turns of wire* in the solenoid. The more turns of wire there are in the solenoid, the greater will be the induced e.m.f.

Fleming's Left-Hand Rule

There is a simple means of working out the relationship of the directions of maget, magnetic field, and induced current in electromagnetic induction. The thumb, forefinger, and second finger of the left hand are held at right angles to each other, thus occupying all three planes in space (Fig. 42). The thumb is placed in the direction of the motion of the magnet (that is, pointing in the direction in which the magnet is moving); the forefinger then shows the direction of the magnetic field asso-

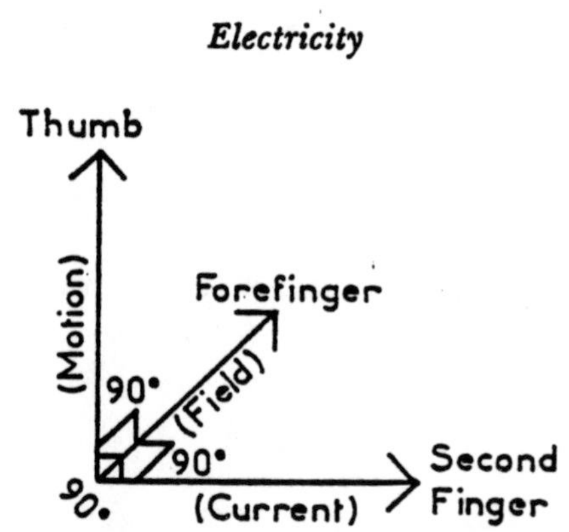

Figure 42. Fleming's left-hand rule.

ciated with the magnet, and the second finger will indicate the direction in which the induced current will flow.

Self-induced E.M.F.

The principles of the electromagnet (the production of a magnetic field by electricity) and electromagnetic induction (the production of an electric current by fluctuating magnetism) can be correlated. In Figure 39 a magnetic field will be produced in the soft iron core by closing the switch and causing a current to flow around the solenoid. During the short time after closing the switch, the current from the battery will grow from zero to a maximum, steady value. The induced magnetic field will also grow from zero to a maximum, at the same rate as the current. For the time it takes for this maximum to be reached, the solenoid will be lying in a changing magnetic field. Once the maximum is reached, both current and magnetic field will remain steady.

We are concerned with what happens during this initial period of time: A changing magnetic field will induce an e.m.f. in a solenoid. The solenoid which is lying in this particular changing magnetic field is already carrying a current, the current that is inducing the magnetic field. The e.m.f. (and, hence, current) that is induced will be superimposed on the original current in the solenoid. The superimposed e.m.f. will cause a current to flow in the opposite direction to the original. Part of the original current will, therefore, be canceled.

When the switch in the circuit is opened and the original current in the solenoid is cut off, the reverse process to the above occurs. The current, and therefore the magnetic field, falls from maximum to zero, thus creating once more a changing magnetic field. As the direction of magnitude of the magnetic field has reversed, the direction of the induced current will also reverse. This time the induced current will flow in the same direction as the original current and tend to boost it instead of canceling it. This phenomenon causes the current to continue flowing for a fraction of a second after the supply has been cut off.

The process of inducing a current in the wire which is itself carrying the inducing current is known as self-induction or back e.m.f. If an alternating current is supplied to the solenoid instead of a direct current, this will create the same effect as if the direct current were being rapidly switched on and off to produce the above series of effects.

Mutual Induction

In the setup shown in Figure 43, the following course of events can occur: An alternating current is passed through the solenoid *A*, producing a changing magnetic field in the soft iron core of *A*. The soft iron core of solenoid *B* lies in the field produced by the core of solenoid *A*. It will therefore have exactly the same, changing, magnetic field induced in it. The changing magnetic field induced in core *B* will induce an e.m.f. in solenoid *B*. This induced e.m.f. will register on the recording meter as the current

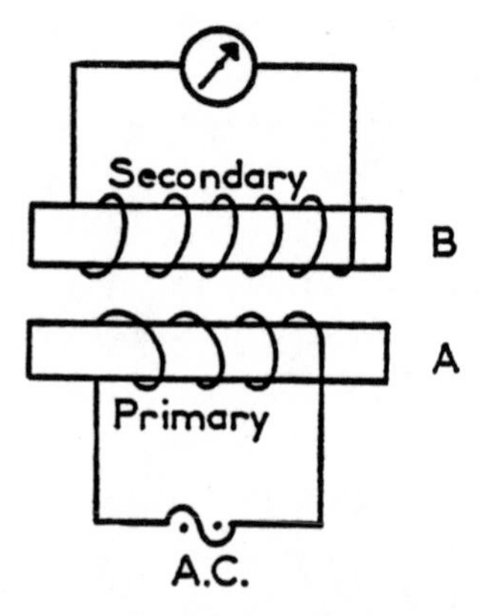

Figure 43. Mutual induction.

flows. Thus, with no electrical connection between them, electrical energy has passed from solenoid *A* to solenoid *B*.

This process is known as mutual induction. Mutual induction is the principle of the transformer. The solenoid *A* is known as the primary, and solenoid *B* is known as the secondary. The secondary e.m.f. is actually induced via the magnetic effects of the two cores, but it is customary to simplify matters by saying that the secondary e.m.f. is induced directly from the primary.

Transformers

A transformer is a device to change the voltage supplied from a higher to a lower value, or from a lower to a higher. Transformers work on alternating current. They work on the principle of mutual induction.

Transformer Law

The ratio of the number of turns of wire on the primary to the number of turns on the secondary is the same as the ratio of the voltage on the primary to the voltage on the secondary. Example: If the secondary has three times as many turns as the primary, then the voltage on the secondary will be three times greater than that on the primary.

The explanation for this is as follows: Every coil of wire will cut across exactly the same number of lines of magnetic flux as every other coil. As the e.m.f. induced depends on the number of lines of force that are crossed, it follows that every coil of wire will have induced in it exactly the same e.m.f. as every other coil (Fig. 44). Therefore, the more coils of wire there are on the secondary, the greater will be the induced e.m.f. The total induced e.m.f. is equal to the number of coils of wire multiplied by the e.m.f. induced in each one.

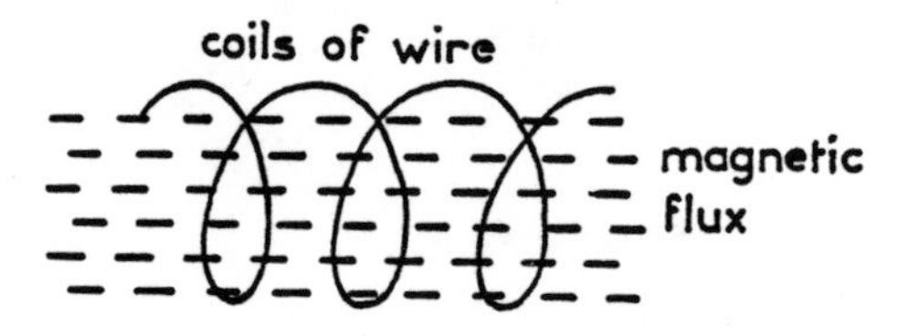

Figure 44. Transformer law.

This state of affairs would appear to be defying the law of conservation of energy: that energy can be neither created nor destroyed, and this is impossible. From the above law, we know that the total energy fed into the primary should equal the total energy taken out of the secondary.

The power formula gives us $P = IV$

power in on primary = power out of secondary

or $$(IV)_1 = (IV)_2$$

Where $(IV)_1$ = the power on the primary;
$(IV)_2$ = the power in the secondary.

We have said that we can get a higher voltage out of the secondary than we put into the primary, and to keep the balance of the equation straight this means that the current in the secondary must be smaller. An example will illustrate this: Suppose the ratio of turns of primary to secondary is 5 : 15 (the secondary has 3 times more turns). The e.m.f. on the primary = 5 volts and the current on primary = 24 amp. As the ratio is 5 : 15, the 5 volts put in on the primary will produce 15 volts from the secondary. The formula will now read: $5 \times 24 = 15 \times I_2$

Rearranged $$I_2 = \frac{5 \times 24}{15} = 8 \text{ amp.}$$

Thus, although the voltage has been increased by a factor of 3 between primary and secondary, the current has been reduced by a factor of 3, keeping the balance between power in and power out. The transformer law can be written as an equation:

$$\frac{N_1}{N_2} = \frac{V_1}{V_2}$$

Where N_1 = the number of turns on the primary;
N_2 = the number of turns on the secondary;
V_1 = the voltage on the primary;
V_2 = the voltage on the secondary.

Power Loss on Transformers

Theoretically, the power put into a transformer on the primary side is the same as the power removed from the transformer

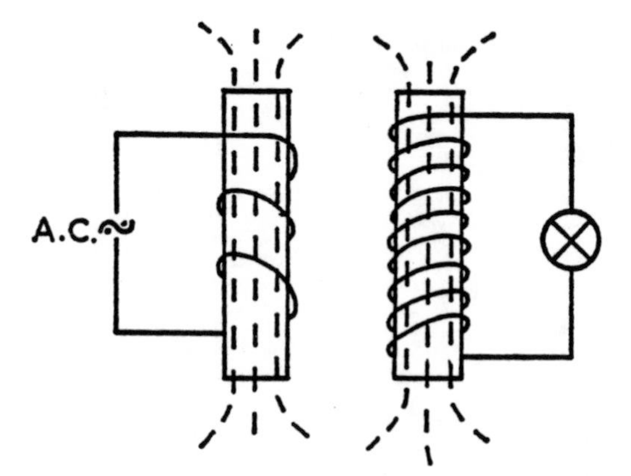

Figure 45. Magnetic power loss.

on the secondary side. In practice, there is a loss of power, as heat, between the two.

Magnetic Losses

As can be seen in Figure 45, a lot of power is lost from this system by way of wasted magnetic flux.

1. *Closed-Core (Doughnut) Transformer*

More of the magnetic flux is channeled into the useful sections of the core, but some is still wasted (Fig. 46).

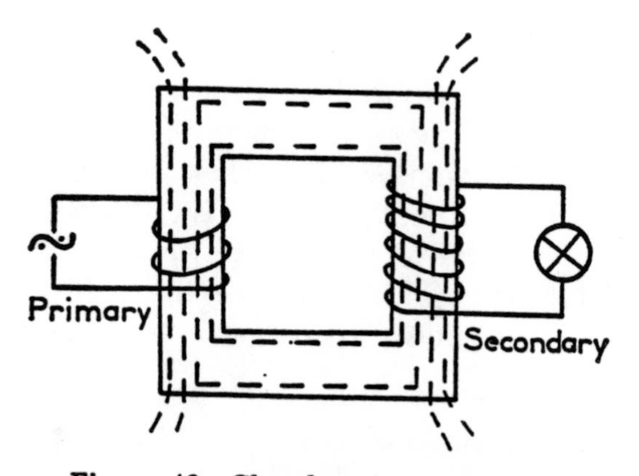

Figure 46. Closed-core transformer.

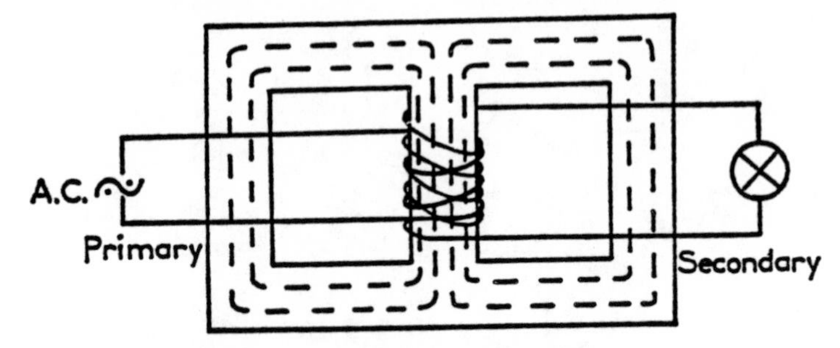

Figure 47. Shell-type transformer.

2. *Shell-type Transformer*

In the shell-type transformer the magnetic flux is channeled around the core of the transformer and the minimum is lost (Fig. 47).

Electrical Losses

1. *Copper Losses*

This is power loss due to the resistance of the copper wire used in the windings. This form of loss is minimized by making the wires of a larger cross section to reduce the resistance. The wire cannot, however be too large in cross section or the equipment will become too bulky. The wire on the winding which carries less voltage (for example, the secondary on a step-down transformer) must be of larger cross section, since it has the larger current to carry.

2. *Eddy Currents*

In a transformer core which is made from a solid block of metal, the magnetic field passing through the core induces side currents, or eddy currents (Fig. 48). These constitute a power loss, again in the form of heat. This loss is overcome by making the core of layers of silicon steel insulated from each other. This is called a laminated core. The silicon steel has high permeability and low retentivity and thus makes a good electromagnet.

3. *Hysteresis Losses*

This is a loss of power due to the inability of the magnetic domains to align themselves at the same rate as the alternating

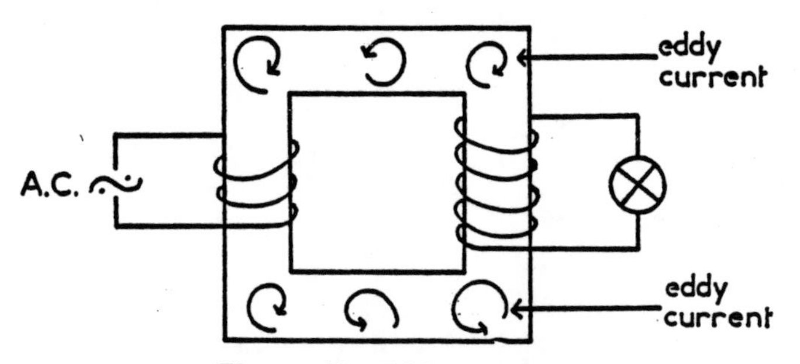

Figure 48. Eddy currents.

current changes direction. Figure 49 shows the following sequence: The current is switched on, and both current and magnetism increase along line *A*. They both reach a maximum at the same time. In other words, the maximum number of magnetic domains are aligned at the same time that the maximum current is reached. The current, being alternating, now reverses its direction and begins to decrease. This causes the atomic domains to begin to reverse their alignment.

But there is a slight delay in the time between the current reversing and the domains beginning to reverse. Thus, when the current reaches zero, there are still some domains which have not fully reversed. This is called the residual magnetism and means that the magnet is not working at full power in synchronization with the current. The cycle thus follows line *B*.

When the current reverses itself again, it follows line C. Since

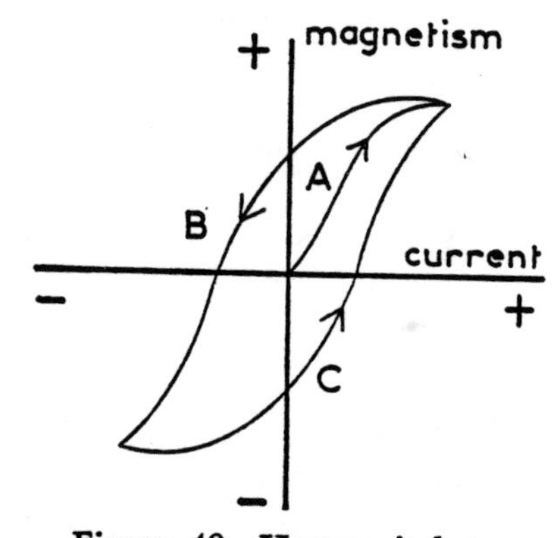

Figure 49. Hysteresis loss.

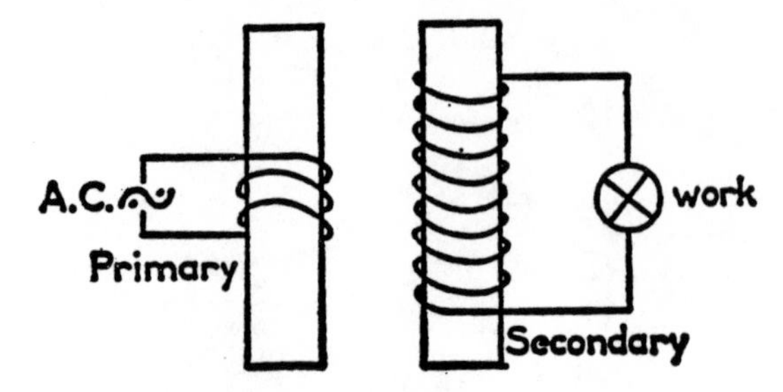

Figure 50. Step-up transformer.

the current and the magnetism never again reach zero at the same time, line *A* is not followed again. Hysteresis losses are minimized by using the special alloy mentioned in the laminated core. It has been found by experience that this is an alloy least likely to suffer hysteresis loss.

Types of Transformer

1. *Step-up Transformer*

A step-up transformer changes the voltage from a lower to a higher value. The secondary has more turns than the primary (Fig. 50). Example: This type is used to step up the domestic supply to the high kV required for x-ray production.

2. *Step-down Transformer*

A step-down transformer changes the supply from a higher value to a lower one (Fig. 51). Example: This type is used in an x-ray set to reduce the voltage supplied to the filament heating circuit of the tube.

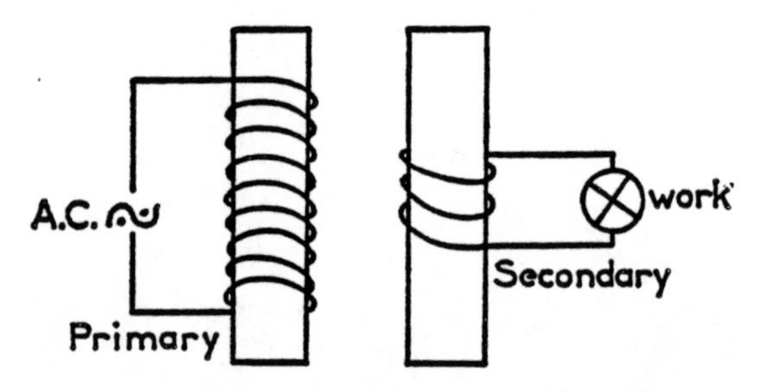

Figure 51. Step-down transformer.

3. *Autotransformer*

An autotransformer can serve as either a step-up or a step-down transformer. Physical factors, however, limit its transformation ratio (ratio between the primary and secondary voltages) to fairly close ranges. For example: An autotransformer could have a transformation ratio of, say, 1 : 2 but not 1 : 200.

In an autotransformer a single winding serves as both primary and secondary. The current is fed into part of the coil, this induces a magnetic field in the whole of the core. The magnetic field in the core induces an e.m.f. in the whole of the coil (Fig. 52). The current induced in the primary part of the winding will be in the reverse direction to the original current. This means that the primary part of the winding carries a smaller current than the rest of it. Part of the inducing current has been cancelled. With the arrangement shown, the size of the secondary can be varied and the voltage tapped off at any point required.

Autotransformer Law

This law is exactly the same as the transformer law. The fact that there is only a single winding instead of a separate primary and secondary makes no difference to the relationships between the primary and the secondary.

$$\frac{N_1}{N_2} = \frac{V_1}{V_2}$$

Transformer Efficiency

Transformer efficiency is the ratio of the power transferred to the secondary to the power put in on the primary.

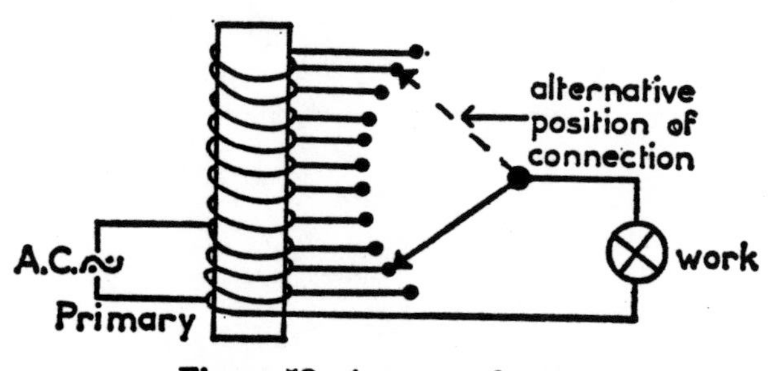

Figure 52. Autotransformer.

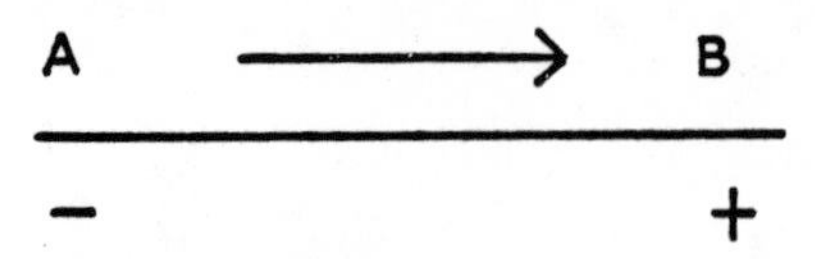

Figure 53.

$$\text{Or } \frac{\text{power available on secondary}}{\text{power put into primary}} \times 100 = \text{efficiency } \%$$

Example: power on primary = 100 volts × 5 amp
= 500 watts;
power from secondary = 480 volts × 0.8 amp
= 384 watts.

$$\text{efficiency} = \frac{384}{500} \times 100 = 77\%$$

There is a loss of 23% efficiency between primary and secondary.

Alternating Current

Direct current is a flow of electricity that moves in one direction only, that is, from a region of high negative potential to one of low negative potential (from negative to positive). Figure 53 shows that *A* is always negative with respect to *B*; therefore, the current always flows from *A* to *B*. With alternating current the positive and negative terminals constantly reverse themselves so that the current flows first from *A* to *B*, then from *B* to *A*, then from *A* to *B*, and so on. This can be shown on a graph (Fig. 54).

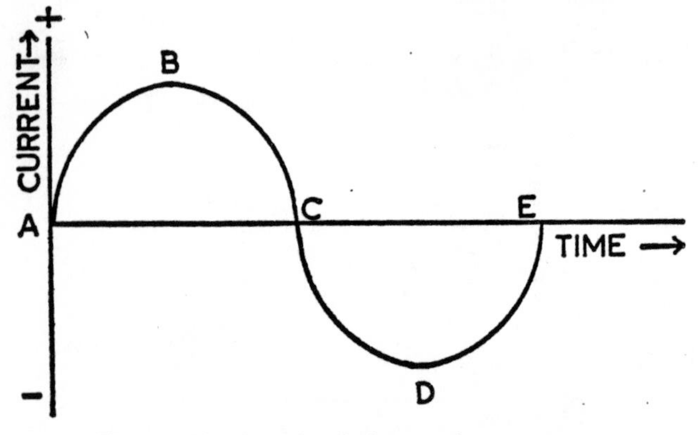

Figure 54. Graph of alternating current.

On the graph the current is switched on at *A* and grows to its maximum value at *B*. When *B* is reached, the current reverses, falls to zero at *C*, then grows to a maximum in the other direction at *D*. It then reverses again and grows to a maximum in the original direction, and so on.

In the ordinary household electrical supply, the current reverses itself sixty times each minute. The current is said to be supplied at a frequency of 60 cps.

Properties of Alternating Current

With direct current there are three factors involved: potential difference, current strength, and resistance. With alternating current the same three factors are involved with slight variations.

1. *Potential Difference and Current Strength*

The magnitude of a direct current or voltage can be stated as a single value. For example: the current is 12 amp or the potential difference is 8 volts.

Effective Current or Voltage. For the purposes of explanation, only current will be referred to, but each comment also applies to potential difference values. The value of an alternating current is not the same from moment to moment, its magnitude rises and falls as its direction reverses. Since it is impossible to specify the value of the current for every fraction of a second, some way must be found of indicating an average, or effective, value. This is done by comparing the heating effect of an alternating current with that of a direct current of known value. This value is then known as the effective current.

The effective current strength of an alternating current is that alternating current which would produce the same heating effect as a comparable direct current. Example: If an alternating current is found to produce X calories of heat then the effective current strength of that alternating current is the same as the current strength of a direct current which would also produce X calories of heat.

There is a simple relationship between the peak value of the alternating current and the effective value of the alternating current:

effective value = 0.707 × peak value

Similarly for potential difference:

effective voltage = 0.707 × peak voltage

If, on the other hand, the effective current is known and it is required to find the peak value the equation now reads

peak current = 1.41 × effective current value.

2. *Opposition to Current*

In a circuit supplied by direct current the opposition to the current is a simple matter of resistance. When an alternating current is supplied, the constant reversal of the current causes other, complicating effects. The total opposition to alternating current is called impedance and is given the symbol Z.

Impedance is composed of a combination of resistance and reactance. Resistance is the same as the resistance met with in direct current supply. Reactance can be either inductive reactance, which is caused by the inductive effects of the alternating current causing a changing magnetic field, and opposes the current; or it can be capacitive reactance, which is the effect caused by a capacitor in an alternating current circuit, and tends to boost the current.

When calculating the total impedance, or opposition to current, in an alternating current circuit, it is therefore important to know what components the circuit contains, as they may either oppose or boost the current. The relationship between the various components of impedance is not simple and will not be dealt with here.

Advantages of Alternating Current

Transformers can be operated directly from an alternating current supply. It is much easier to transmit electricity over long distances using high voltage and low current strength. This is practically more possible with alternating current than with direct current. The physical limitations on direct-current generators make this difference.

Circuits

The components of a circuit can be connected to each other in series, in parallel, or in a combination of both of these.

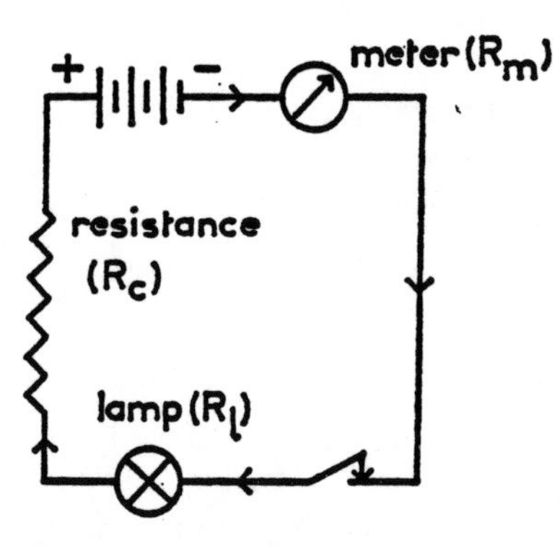

Figure 55. Resistances in series.

1. *Series Circuits*

a. *Resistance in Series.* When components are connected so that the current flows through each of them in turn, they are said to be connected in series. It is often necessary to know the total resistance to the current in such a circuit. In Figure 55 the current is provided by a battery, so the only opposition to the current will be resistance, since a battery always supplies direct current.

The total resistance is made up of the individual resistances added together. This is logical, as the current must pass through each one in turn and will be offered resistance by each one. Resistance will be offered by the meter, the lamp, and the circuit itself, which is represented by the resistance symbol in the diagram.

$$\text{total resistance} = \text{resistance of (meter + lamp + circuit)}$$

$$R_T = R_M + R_L + R_C.$$

Example: lamp (L) = 5 ohms resistance;
meter (M) = 12 ohms resistance;
circuit (C) = 4 ohms resistance.

$$\text{total resistance} = (5 + 12 + 4) \text{ ohms}$$
$$= 21 \text{ ohms}$$

b. *Capacitors in Series.* These behave in a different way to resistors in series (Fig. 56). The easiest way to show the difference is to write it as an equation:

$$\frac{1}{\text{total capacitance}} = \frac{1}{C_1} + \frac{1}{C_2} + \frac{1}{C_3}$$

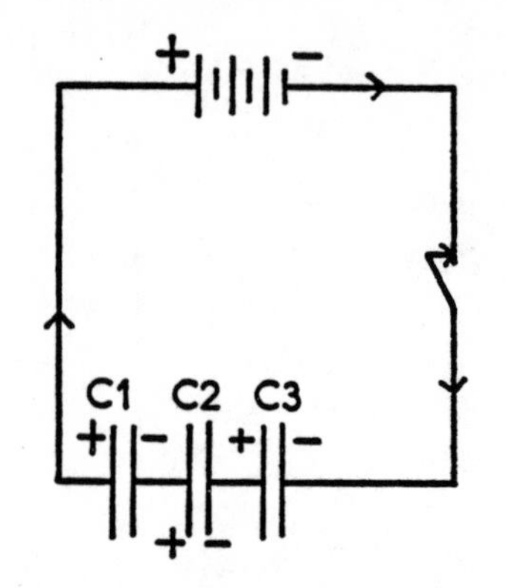

Figure 56. Capacitors in series.

Where C_1, C_2 and C_3 are the individual capacitances connected in series.

Example: Suppose $C_1 = 5$ farads capacitance;
$C_2 = 10$ farads and
$C_3 = 5$ farads.

$$\frac{1}{\text{total capacitance}} = \left(\frac{1}{5} + \frac{1}{10} + \frac{1}{5}\right) \text{farads}$$

$$= \left(\frac{2 + 1 + 2}{10}\right) \text{farads}$$

$$= \frac{1}{2} \text{farad}$$

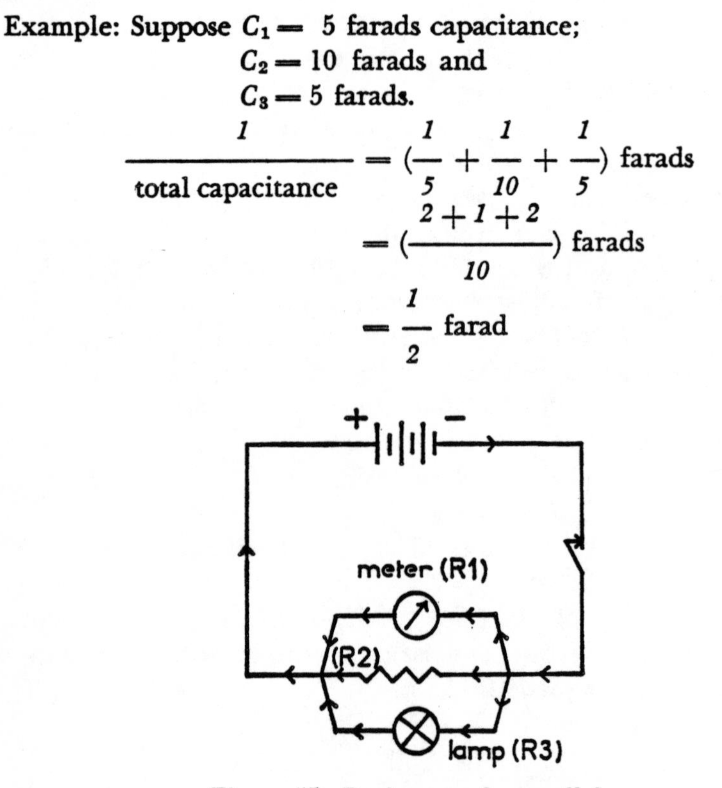

Figure 57. Resistances in parallel.

2. *Parallel Circuits*

a. *Resistances in Parallel.* When the components of the circuit are connected parallel to the main circuit, as in Figure 57, the total opposition to the current will obviously be different from what it was in the series connection. Instead of having to pass through each component in turn, the current will split and pass through all the components at the same time. The relationship between resistances in parallel is similar to that between capacitances in series:

$$\frac{1}{\text{total resistance}} = \frac{1}{R_1} + \frac{1}{R_2} + \frac{1}{R_3}.$$

Example: Suppose $R_1 = 5$ ohms, $R_2 = 10$ ohms, and $R_3 = 5$ ohms.

Let total resistance $= R_T$.

$$\frac{1}{R_T} = \left(\frac{1}{5} + \frac{1}{10} + \frac{1}{5}\right) \text{ ohms}$$

$$= \left(\frac{2+1+2}{10}\right) \text{ ohms}$$

$$= \frac{1}{2} \text{ ohm.}$$

(Imagine the current as water running through a pipe. If the water has three pipes to run through instead of one there is much less resistance to its passage.)

b. *Capacitors in Parallel.* Capacitors in parallel behave in the

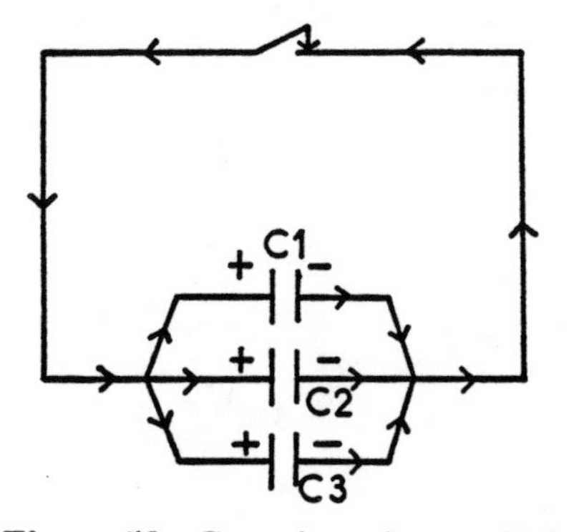

Figure 58. Capacitors in parallel.

same way as do resistors in series (Fig. 58); that is, they add to each other so that the total capacitance in a parallel circuit is the sum of all the capacitances in that circuit. Example: Suppose there are three capacitances in a circuit wired parallel to each other and they have values of 2, 5, and 25 farads.

$$\begin{aligned}\text{total capacitance} &= (2 + 5 + 25) \text{ farads} \\ &= 32 \text{ farads}\end{aligned}$$

3. *Mixed Circuits*

When circuits contain components some of which are connected in series and some in parallel, care must be taken to calculate their total effect on the current according to how they are connected (Fig. 59).

Three-Wire Electrical Supply

Electricity arrives as high voltage and before it can be supplied to homes, it is stepped down, by a transformer, to a manageable voltage. The current is brought into the home by a three-wire system (Fig. 60). The two outside wires are live and the middle one is neutral (grounded). The potential difference between the two live wires is 230 volts and between the neutral and either of the live wires is 115 volts. If a 230 volt supply is needed, then the equipment is connected across the two live wires. If a 115 volt supply is needed, the equipment is connected across one live wire and ground (neutral).

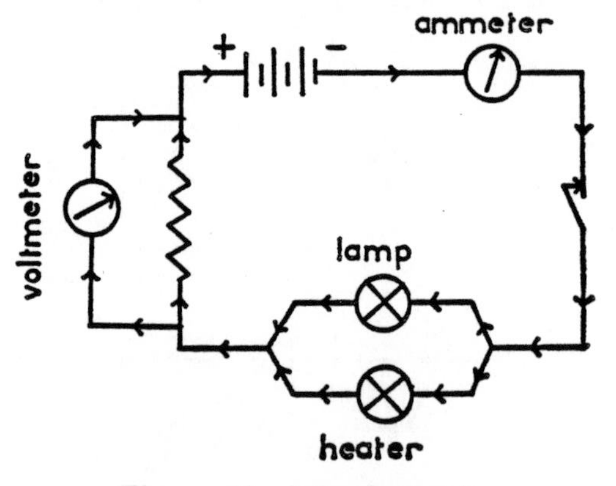

Figure 59. Mixed circuit.

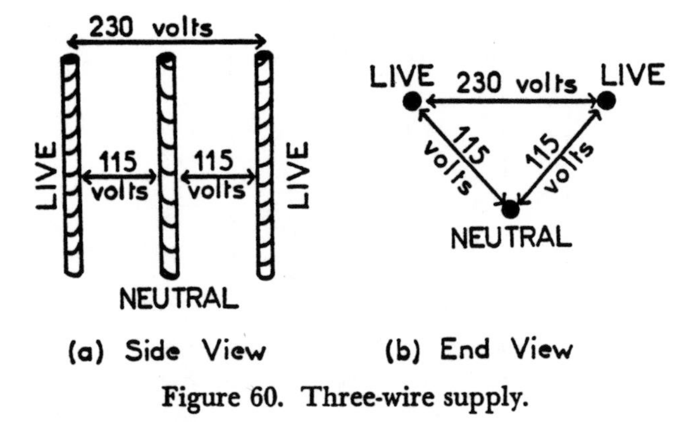

Figure 60. Three-wire supply.

Galvanometer

A galvanometer is an instrument used in the measurement of electricity. The way in which it measures electricity depends upon its position in the electrical circuit.

1. *Ammeter*

When a galvanometer is connected in series with the circuit, it measures current and is called an ammeter (Fig. 61). So as not to interfere with the flow of electricity in the circuit (a meter is for measuring only and should not interfere), the ammeter must have only a very small resistance. The two points which must, therefore, be noted when using a galvanometer as an ammeter are that it must be connected in series and that it must have the smallest possible resistance.

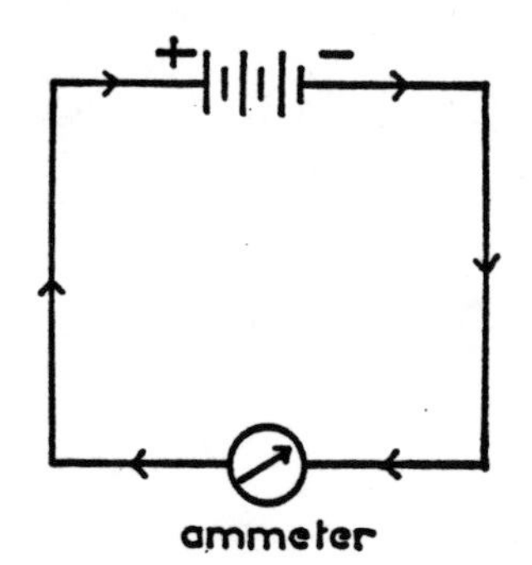

Figure 61. Ammeter connection.

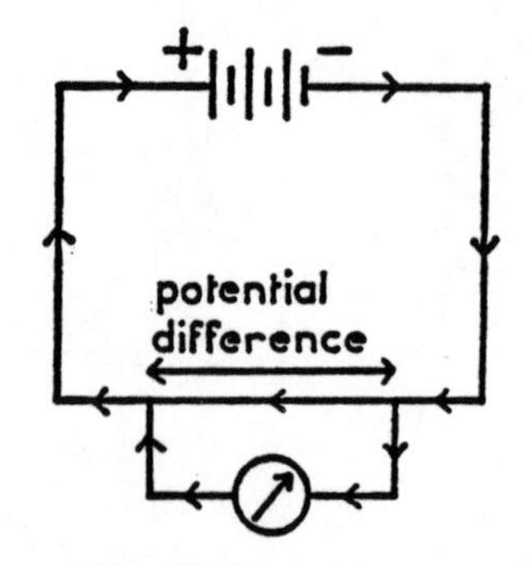

Figure 62. Voltmeter connection.

2. *Voltmeter*

A voltmeter is a galvanometer being used to measure the potential drop between two points in a circuit (Fig. 62). To be used as a voltmeter, a galvanometer must be connected in parallel with the circuit because the voltmeter measures the drop in potential between two stated points only and must be directly connected between these two. The only way to do this is in parallel. It must also have a very high resistance because a parallel path with a low resistance would cause diversion of electricity from the main circuit. Electricity will always take the path of least resist-

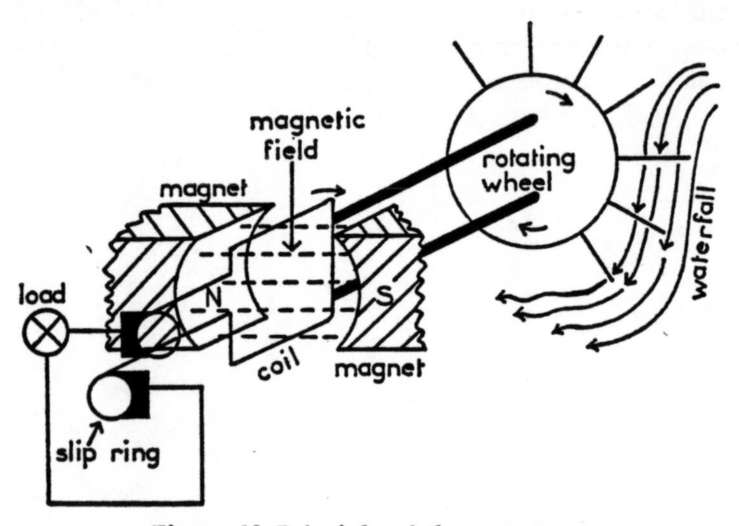

Figure 63. Principle of the generator.

ance. This would interfere with the main circuit and defeat the object of the galvanometer, to measure.

Electric Generator

An electric generator, or dynamo, is a machine that converts mechanical energy to electrical energy. For example, the mechanical energy used may be steam, a waterfall, or even, man power. In Figure 63 the waterfall provides the power to rotate the coil.

When a conductor and a magnetic field move relative to one another, an electromotive force is induced in the conductor and a current will flow in the circuit. It does not matter whether the one moves and the other remains stationary or they both move, so long as they move relative to each other. The electric generator works on the principle of a stationary magnetic field reacting with a moving conductor. The moving conductor is in the form of a coil of wire, either end of which is connected into a circuit in a special way. The coil is rotated in the magnetic field of a strong, direct-current magnet. In Figure 64 the rotating mechanism is the force of the waterfall. The current generated is passed into the circuit by means of a slip-ring connection.

In Figure 64a the coil of wire is moving in the same plane as the field between the magnets. It is not cutting across any lines of magnetic force and so no e.m.f. is induced in the circuit. In Figure 64b the coil has now rotated so that it is cutting across the magnetic field and an e.m.f. is induced. The direction in which the current will flow can be found by applying Fleming's left-hand rule.

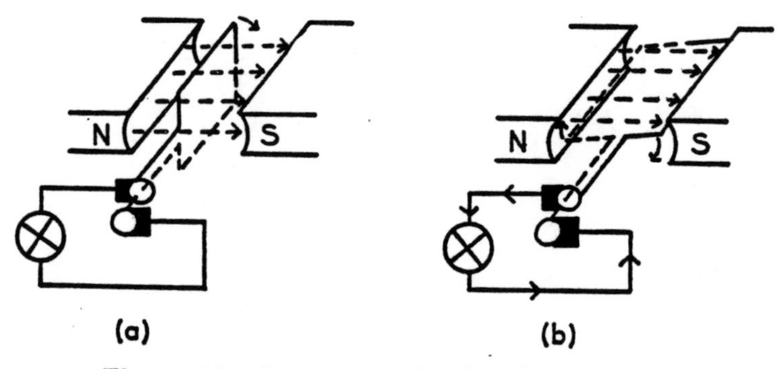

Figure 64. Current production by generator.

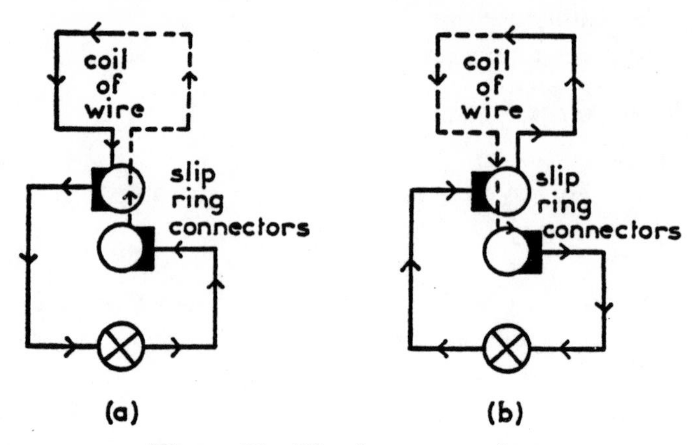

Figure 65. Slip-ring connection.

Alternating-Current Generator

When the induced current is led into the circuit by way of a slip-ring connector, an alternating current is produced (Fig. 65).

Direct-Current Generator

If the slip-ring connector is replaced by a split ring, then direct current will be produced (Fig. 66). Every half revolution of the coil causes the current to reverse its direction. However, the split ring has also reversed its position and is now in contact with the opposite connector. The result is that the current continues to

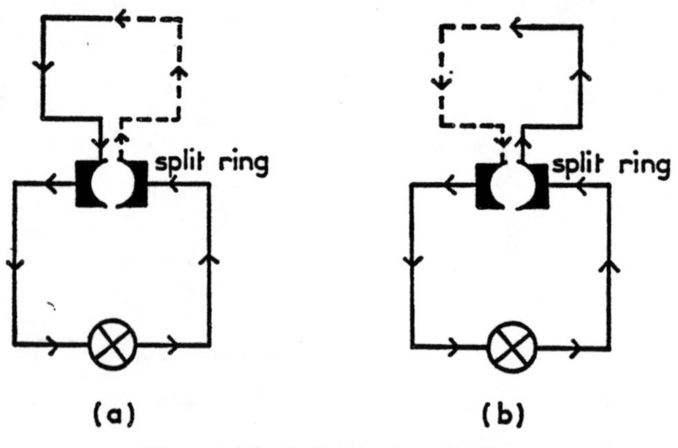

Figure 66. Split-ring conection.

be supplied to the circuit in the original direction. A direct current has been produced.

The split ring may be divided into more than two sections, each attached to a loop of wire. As the loops rotate in the magnetic field each will have a current generated in it at a slightly different angle to all the others. This will produce a smoother direct current than will a single coil. The multiple split ring is called a split-ring commutator.

Electric Motors

An electric motor is a machine which does the opposite to an electric generator. It converts electrical energy to mechanical energy. The principle is that current passing through a coil is combined with a magnetic field to produce motion of the coil. A wire carrying a current (into the page in Fig. 67) is placed in the field between two magnets. The current passing through the wire produces a magnetic field around the wire in the direction shown by the arrows.

At *A* the magnetic fields are in opposition and will partly cancel each other. The field is therefore weakened at *A*. At *B* the magnetic fields are in the same direction and will repel each other. There is, therefore, a stronger field at *B* than at *A*, and the wire will be pushed in the direction of *A*. The combination of the two magnetic fields, one from the wire and one from the magnets, has produced motion of the wire.

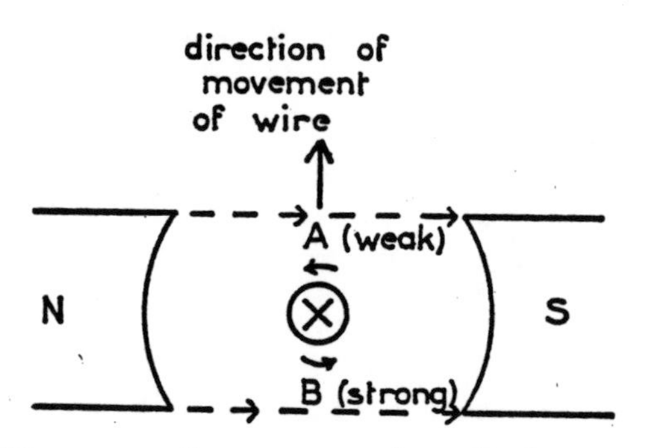

Figure 67. Movement of current-carrying wire in a magnetic field.

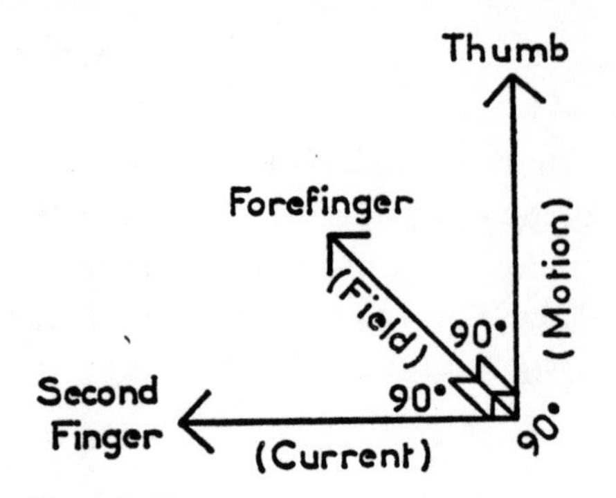

Figure 68. Right-hand motor rule.

The Right-Hand Motor Rule

Just as Fleming's left-hand rule can be applied to generators to find the direction of the current produced, so the right-hand rule can be applied to motors to find the direction of the motion produced. The thumb, first finger, and second finger of the right hand are held at right angles to each other (Fig. 68). The first finger is pointed in the direction of the magnetic field (from the magnets); the second finger is pointed in the direction of the current in the wire, and the thumb then indicates the direction in which the wire will move.

Principle of a Simple Electric Motor

Figure 69a shows a coil of wire carrying a current in a magnetic field, while Figure 69b shows the same coil in cross section. The combination of magnetic fields produces a strong field at *B* and a weak field at *A*, causing the wire to move upward. A strong

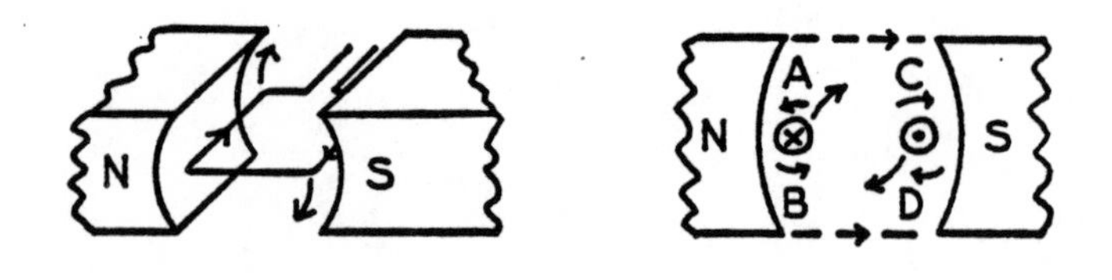

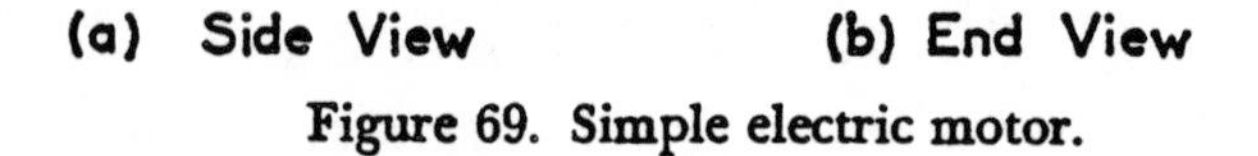

Figure 69. Simple electric motor.

field at *C* and a weak field at *D* causes that wire to move downward. The result is that the coil as a whole rotates. The coil is called an armature.

Back E.M.F. of the Motor

The fact that the armature is moving in a magnetic field induces a back e.m.f. in the armature. The current produced by this is superimposed on the current in the armature and partly cancels it. This means that the current needed to run the motor is reduced.

Glossary

A.C.: alternating current.

Alpha particle: a group of four particles (2 protons and 2 neutrons) emitted from an unstable nucleus.

Alpha ray: a stream of alpha particles emitted from a large group of unstable nuclei.

Alternating current: electric current that continuously reverses its direction of flow. This is called reversing its polarity.

Ammeter: a meter for measuring current strength.

Amplitude: the height of a wave from its position of rest on the baseline to either the crest or the trough.

Atom: the basic unit from which everything else is built.

Atomic number: the number of protons in the nucleus. This is also the same as the number of electrons in orbit around the nucleus of a stable atom.

Atomic weight: the weight of an atom compared with the weight of an atom of carbon.

Back e.m.f.: an induced e.m.f. producing a current in the opposite direction to the original current.

Battery: a collection (or battery) of cells producing electrical energy by converting chemical energy.

Beta particle: an electron moving in a path other than its atomic orbit.

Beta ray: a stream of beta particles.

Binding energy: the energy associated with a particular shell of a particular element.

Capacitor: a device for storing electricity.

Capacitance: the amount of charge a capacitor can store.

Charge: an ionized particle. If an electron is removed from an atom, two charges are formed. The displaced electron is the negative charge and the rest of the atom is the positive charge. Sometimes the electron becomes attached to an otherwise neutral atom, thus giving it a negative charge.

Chemical property: the way in which an element or compound reacts chemically with other elements or compounds.

Chemical symbol: a shorthand form of naming the elements; for example, lead is Pb and carbon is C.

Closed circuit: a complete path through which a current can flow.

Circuit: an arrangement of components forming a completed pathway for the flow of electric current.

Circuit diagram: a schematic drawing of a circuit.

Compound: an association of two or more elements to form another substance. The new substance (the compound) has different properties to any of the elements involved in its formation.

Condenser: another name for a capacitor.

Conduction: the method by which heat is transferred through a solid body.

Conductor: a substance that allows the passage of electricity.

Convection: the method by which heat is transferred through a fluid.

Current electricity: the movement of electric charges from one place to another. Current flows from negative to positive.

Decay: the transformation of one element into another by the emission of alpha- or beta-particles from the nucleus.

Deuterium: "heavy" hydrogen, that is, hydrogen with a neutron added to the nucleus.

Deuteron: the nucleus of a deuterium atom.

Diamagnetic material: a substance that is repelled by magnetism.

Dielectric: the material that insulates the two plates of a capacitor from each other.

Dielectric constant: a number indicating the efficiency of a dielectric as an insulator. The higher the number, the greater the efficiency.

Direct current: a current of electricity flowing in one direction only.

Direct ionization: ionization brought about by the direct action of the ionizing agency.

Eddy current: an unwanted current produced in the core of an electromagnet if it is not laminated.

Electric motor: a device for converting electrical energy to mechanical energy.

Electricity: the transfer of energy by means of charged particles, or the build up of static charges.

Electrification: the process of charging a body.

Electrodynamics: the study of current electricity.

Electromagnetic radiation: a means of transmitting energy from place to place without the use of particles.

Electromagnetic spectrum: the range of energies of electromagnetic radiations.

Electromagnet: a magnet created by passing an electric current through a coil of wire. A core of magnetic material is placed in the center of the coil to concentrate the magnetic field.

Electron: a minute negatively charged particle that moves in orbit around the nucleus of the atom.

Electroscope: an instrument that can be used to detect the passage of ionizing radiation by the leakage of charge from its leaves.

Electrostatics: the study of static electricity.

Element: the simplest chemical substances.

E.m.f.: electromotive force. Other names are potential difference and voltage.

eV: electron volt. The energy acquired by an electron in falling through a potential difference of 1 volt.

Ferromagnetic material: material that makes a good magnet.

Field: an area of influence.

Fluid: a substance that flows, a liquid or a gas.

Force: an influence that tends to alter the state of a body; that is, either push it from a static position or stop it from moving.

Frequency: the number of waves per second.

Galvanometer: an instrument for measuring electricity. Connected in series, it measures current strength; connected in parallel, it measures voltage.

Gamma ray: when an unstable nucleus has emitted an alpha- or beta-particle it is often left with excess energy. This is given out as a gamma ray. It is usually associated with beta-emission rather than alpha-emission.

Generator: a device for converting mechanical energy to electrical energy.

Ground: the earth (or ground) is regarded as a huge reservoir of electrons. Any charged body connected to ground will become neutralized.

Half-life: the time taken for the radioactivity of a radioisotope to decay to half its original value.

Heat: a form of electromagnetic radiation.

Hysteresis loss: a form of power loss from the core of a transformer.

Impedance: the total effective opposition offered to alternating current.

Indirect ionization: ionization caused secondary to the action of the original ionizing influence, and not by the original ionizing influence itself.

Induction: the process of magnetization or charging without actual contact between the bodies concerned. An induced charge or magnetic pole is always opposite to that of the inducing body.

Insulator: a substance that tends to oppose the passage of electric current.

Inverse square law: the intensity of radiation at any point is inversely proportional to the square of the distance of that point from the source of radiation.

Ionization: when an electron is removed from the orbit of a neutral atom, the atom is left with an overall positive charge. The positively charged atom is called a positive ion and the electron is called a negative ion.

Ionizing radiation: any form of radiation that causes ionization; for example, alpha- and beta-rays, x-rays, and gamma-rays.

Isobar: any two elements having the same mass number as each other but, of course, a different atomic number.

Isotope: any two atoms of the same element which have different mass numbers to each other but, of course, the same atomic number.

KeV: thousand electron volts.

Kinetic energy: the energy possessed by a body by virtue of its motion.

Lodestone: a naturally occurring magnet. Used by the old mariners as a compass.

Magnetic domain: theoretically, a molecular magnet.

Magnetic Field: the area of magnetic influence around a magnet.

Magnetism: the power to attract or repel other magnetic materials.

Mass number: the total number of protons plus neutrons in the nucleus of an atom.

MeV: million electron volts.

Mixed circuit: an electrical circuit containing components in both series and parallel wiring.

Mixture: an association of two or more chemical substances which, when placed together, do not react with each other but retain their separate identities.

Molecule: the smallest possible particle of a compound.

Motor: a device by which some form of energy is converted to mechanical energy.

Natural magnets: those found already existing in the earth; that is, lodestone and the earth itself.

Neutron: a nuclear particle the size of a proton but carrying no charge.

Nonmagnetic material: a material that cannot be magnetized.

Nuclear decay: an unstable nucleus, such as in a radioisotope, will attempt to reach a stable state by emitting an alpha-particle or by "splitting" a proton or neutron and emitting a beta-particle. In the process its atomic number is altered, therefore its chemical identity is altered.

Nucleus: the central part of an atom containing most of the mass of the atom. It is made up of protons and neutrons.

Ohm's law: the relationship between the potential difference, current strength, and resistance in an electric circuit ($V=I\times R$).

Open circuit: an incomplete electric circuit that will not allow the passage of electric current.

Orbit: the path in which an electron moves around the nucleus of an atom. It is also called a shell.

Parallel circuits: electrical circuits in which the components are connected parallel to each other.

Paramagnetic material: material that can be magnetized but only with difficulty and only weakly.

Periodic table: an arrangement of the elements in order of their atomic numbers so that they fall into chemically and physically similar groups and "periods."

Permanent magnet: a magnet made of material that has high retentivity and low permeability. It is difficult to magnetize, but once magnetized it remains so.

Permeability: the ease with which a material can be magnetized or demagnetized. Substances with high permeability are easy to magnetize and those with low permeability are hard.

Photon theory: that electromagnetic radiation is transferred in photons, or bundles, of energy. These are also called quanta (singular is quantum).

Physical property: the property of a substance relating to its physical state; that is, whether it is a liquid or a gas, its boiling point, etc.

Positron: an unnatural particle the same size as an electron but carrying a positive charge instead of a negative. This particle is manufactured in certain processes of nuclear decay and soon becomes converted to some other form of energy.

Potential difference: the energy available to move a current around an electrical circuit. It is the difference in energy between a point at a high negative potential and some other point at a low negative potential. If the two points are connected to each other, electrons will move from the high negative potential to the low; this constitutes a current flow.

Power: rate of doing work.

Property: a characteristic of a substance.

Proton: a nuclear particle the same size as a neutron and carrying a positive charge. It is approximately 1,850 times larger than an electron.

Quantum theory: the theory that electromagnetic radiation is transferred in quanta, or bundles, of energy. This is really another name for the photon theory.

Radiation: a form of transferring energy across a vacuum.

Radioactive isotope: an unstable isotope. The nucleus tries to reach a stable state by the emission of a particle and, sometimes, energy.

Radioisotope: another name for radioactive isotope.

Resistance: opposition offered to the passage of electric current.

Retentivity: the ability of a magnetic material to retain its magnetism.

Schematic: another name for circuit diagram. A drawing of an electrical circuit.

Series circuit: one in which the components are connected in series (one after the other).

Shell: another name for an orbit. The path of an electron around the nucleus of an atom.

Specific ionization: the amount of ionization caused by a particular ionizing agent in a certain distance in a straight line. A lower energy ionizing agent will cause more ionization in that distance than will a higher energy and, thus, will have a higher specific ionization value than the lower energy.

Static discharge: when the potential difference between two electrodes separated by an insulating material becomes great enough the surplus electrons on the negative electrode cross the gap to the positive electrode in one big burst.

Step-down transformer: a device for reducing voltage.

Step-up transformer: a device for increasing voltage.

Stroking: a method of magnetizing a material.

Temporary magnet: a magnet having a low retentivity.

Transformer: a device for altering voltage.

Valency: the combining power of an element.

Velocity: rate of movement in a specified direction.

Voltmeter: a meter for measuring the potential difference between two points.

Wavelength: the distance from a particular point on a wave to the same point on the next wave; for example, from the crest of one wave to the crest of the next.

Wave theory: the theory that electromagnetic radiation travels in waves.

X-ray: a form of electromagnetic radiation.

Index